SMALL MAN OF NANATAKI

also by the author:
THE HILLS HID US WELL

Kiyoshi Watanabe – Uncle John, the small man of Nanataki.

SMALL MAN OF NANATAKI

The true story of a Japanese who risked his life
to provide comfort for his enemies

LIAM NOLAN

POSTSCRIPT by SIR SELWYN SELWYN-CLARKE
K.B.E., C.M.G., M.C., M.D., F.R.C.P.

E. P. DUTTON & CO., INC.: NEW YORK
1966

For my wife, Oonagh, with gratitude for her
belief, help and encouragement.

AUTHOR'S NOTE

In 1956 I was in Hong Kong as a National Service subaltern. Like anyone else who has ever gone there, I too was fascinated by this tiny colony at the foot of Communist China.

Hong Kong is a place of magic. But I also found it a place of people who had long and horrifying memories that went back to the searing days of wartime. You didn't have to search far or listen for long before you heard the stories of what had happened during the Japanese occupation. I heard many such stories.

But then one day I heard something different. It was vague, and it had something to do with a strange hero from Japan. He was, I was told, an interpreter, and they said his name was Uncle John. That was as much as I heard at the beginning. But there were other snippets at other times, and they all added up to a remarkable and unlikely character who apparently risked his life on numerous occasions so that other men, nominally his enemies, might live. By the time I left Hong Kong to return to England I was more intrigued than ever by what I had heard about this man who was known as Uncle John.

Time, however, dimmed the memory except that on a few occasions I was haunted by the vision of this 20th century Samaritan about whom I had heard so many fragmentary bits of information and praise.

In 1960, while writing 'This Is Your Life' scripts for B.B.C.

Television, I chanced to work on a story which had a Hong Kong wartime background. It was the story of a woman named Ellen Field, and right out of the blue I once again ran across the name of Uncle John. This time, however, I found out his real name too. It was Kiyoshi Watanabe, and all I knew was that he was a Lutheran minister and *might* still be alive in Japan.

With the help of the British Embassy I finally tracked down Rev. Watanabe and invited him to come to London for the television programme. I shall not easily forget the feelings that ran through me when I met for the first time this man I had heard about four years earlier right across the world. It was indeed the same Uncle John.

His appearance on 'This Is Your Life' had a huge effect on many people. I remember well seeing many of the studio audience crying when this man of quite extraordinary gentleness came on. And I remember too the things that happened on the day following the programme. There was the restaurant in the Strand where the waitress hovered about our table staring at the unheeding Uncle John. Finally she bowed low over my shoulder and asked: 'Is this the Japanese gentleman who was on television last night?' I told her it was. She stood up straight again, and by this time Uncle John was aware that something was going on behind him. He turned and smiled up at her and then she said: 'Up until last night I hated every Japanese that ever lived because my brother was tortured by them and died in Hong Kong. But after seeing you, sir, I can never hate them again, because I know now that there must have been good Japanese too. God bless you.'

Going back to his hotel at Lancaster Gate after lunch I explained exactly to Uncle John what it was the waitress had said. We were sitting in an Underground train, and when I looked at his face it was to see tears pouring down his cheeks. I didn't know what to do or say. He was much older than I, and he was unashamedly crying before all the people in the carriage. Then he took out a handkerchief, pressed it to his face and stayed that way for a few minutes. When he looked up, he was smiling. As

viii

he wiped his eyes he said: 'I am glad I am a messenger of peace.'

Minutes later we were standing in the crowded lift taking us to road level at Lancaster Gate station. Uncle John was separated from me, and when the people began to pour out into the street I momentarily lost him. Then I saw a huge red-faced man fighting his way back through the crowd to get to him, and for some strange reason I felt a hint of fear and followed. I got to Uncle John just behind the big man who was holding out his right hand and saying: 'I saw you on television last night, sir. It is a great privilege for me to shake your hand.' Uncle John nodded, but didn't say anything. He was crying again.

This then is the man about whom this book is written. During the nights that I talked to him at his Lancaster Gate hotel, I found myself walking down the same Hong Kong streets with him. And as I questioned him further the sensation became almost eerie, because I too had been at Shamshui Po camp, but in peacetime and many years later. And I too had lived in the same hut where Uncle John had lived—and feared.

As Sir Selwyn Selwyn-Clarke says in his Postscript to this book, there were several Japanese who helped in organising relief for Hong Kong's prisoners of war. This is the story of just one of them.

Liam Nolan
St Albans, 1965.

SMALL MAN OF NANATAKI

CHAPTER I

The bird must have been very hungry because even when the boys broke cover and started to shriek and run in its direction, it just made a little hopping run to another place and kept on pecking at the ground. The stones started hurtling then, and still the bird didn't fly away. The boys—there were five of them —threw all the stones they had in their hands, then stooped and took up more. They were delighted that the bird didn't fly. It wasn't often they had such an accommodating target. The stones showered around the bird. Suddenly one of them struck. It made an odd noise. A sickening dull sound with no sharpness to it. And the bird didn't hop then any more. It just stayed there, legs hidden, belly feathers on the ground, head jerking left and right and the eyes darting with fright.

The boys began to crowd in around the wounded bird. They were just a little frightened, but they were fascinated too. They had wanted to hit the bird, and yet, now that they had done it, they were uneasy. Their chatter died down. One of them, as he drew closer to the bird, stooped again and picked up a small jagged rock. Just at that moment there was a shout from behind them. They all turned, arrested in their slow movement forward by the urgency of the shout and the sound of running feet.

'Get away! Get away all of you and don't touch that bird!'

The running figure sped towards them, in among them, and on to where the bird lay in bewildering pain. The others boys

1

said nothing, but exchanged strained looks. Who was this fellow Watanabe to come shouting orders at them like this? It was none of his business. He was more or less the same age as they. If they wanted to throw stones at stupid birds who wouldn't get out of the way, it was no concern of his. But none of them said these things aloud.

Kiyoshi Watanabe had the wounded bird nestled softly in his palm. For a moment he forgot the boys. All his thoughts were on the frightened creature he held in his hand. He whispered to the bird, talked softly to it as he rubbed a gentle forefinger over its head. 'Hsshh,' he said, 'Ssshh. There you are now. There. There. You'll be all right. I won't hurt you. There.'

Then he became aware of the five boys again. They were standing in a semicircle looking at him.

'You should be ashamed,' he shouted, 'look at what you've done. You've wounded this little creature. You've hurt it. I suppose you'll all feel very brave now and walk like tall men in Nanataki tonight because you have crippled a bird. Well, if you want to know something, I think Nanataki should be ashamed of you.'

As soon as he said it Kiyoshi Watanabe was afraid. There were five of them, and any one of them could have beaten him in a fight. He was no fighter. He dreaded pain. But now he had let his tongue talk him into a situation where the boys might turn on him and give him a beating for his taunts.

They didn't. To his surprise they turned and walked away quietly without saying a word. He looked after them for a few seconds, and then a fluttering movement in his hand brought his gaze back to the bird. In a little while he couldn't see the feathery bundle at all. The tears dropped away from his eyes and fell in little crystal globules onto the feathers.

Kiyoshi walked away blindly from the place, looking for somewhere to leave the cripple. There wasn't anything he could do to mend the tiny broken bones, but he thought that if he left the bird in some secluded spot, other birds might come along and help in some way. Just how he had no idea. When he got

2

away from the road, he gently put the bird at the bottom of a bush.

Then he walked home. Why did people want to hurt and maim? He had no answer. Cruelty was beyond his understanding. Later on, when his older brother Hidezi came in, Kiyoshi asked him the question. Hidezi didn't know the answer either. But Kiyoshi knew that Hidezi would be able to supply at least some part of the remedy before he was much older, for Hidezi was studying to be a doctor.

The occasions on which Hidezi returned from the University to spend the holidays with his parents were times of great rejoicing. The young medical student was fêted in Nanataki. Kiyoshi was always a little uneasy until he could get Hidezi by himself. The youngster listened avidly to the stories Hidezi told about Japan's great capital city, its people, its customs and its University life. Kiyoshi knew that he himself would never get the opportunity to go to University because his father had come to the edge of bankruptcy in the effort to pay Hidezi's fees. Not that Kiyoshi felt any bitterness about it; he was quite content to listen and he was happy for Hidezi.

And then, one holiday, Hidezi came home bringing with him a strange book.

'Kiyoshi,' he said, 'I've got something here which I think you should read.'

'A book of learning?' Kiyoshi enquired.

'In a way, yes,' his brother answered. 'But it is a strange book. It is called The Bible and is all about a Western religion called Christianity. I do not understand all of it myself, but it is interesting. Here, see what you can make of it.'

He tossed the book to Kiyoshi and walked away. Kiyoshi wandered off on his own, eager to see the contents of this strange new book. At first he could make nothing of it. He had never heard of this Jesus Christ, and some of the things attributed to him were just too fantastic to believe. He was both intrigued and baffled, and when he spoke to his twenty-four year old brother, Hidezi tried to cover up his own bafflement

3

with a veneer of cynicism. Kiyoshi went away on his own again and read on. There was something about the book which compelled him to finish reading it. And when he came to the end, one phrase in particular kept repeating itself in his head. Try as he might, he could not dismiss it. 'Man shall not live by bread alone, but by every word that proceedeth out of the mouth of God.'

For some strange reason this impressed him greatly. He could not quite understand it; indeed to a Buddhist such as he, it expressed thoughts which were, to say the least, peculiar. He wanted to know a lot of things. There were many why's and who's and how's, and he desperately needed to have the answers. There was nobody in Nanataki who could help him, because there were no Christians in the village. Kiyoshi would have to bottle up his curiosity until such time as he would be able to contact somebody who lived according to this strange new religion.

When eventually Kiyoshi exhausted the educational facilities available to him in Nanataki village, he persuaded his father and mother to allow him to go and live in Kumamoto, a city about eleven hour's journey away. There he hoped to get a daytime job which would allow him to go to school at night.

It was only after long tiring trudgings around the city streets that at last he discovered a doctor who had patience enough to listen to this keen-faced village boy.

'So you want a job?'

'Yes sir, please. Can you help me sir?'

'Why didn't you stay in Nanataki and get a job there?'

'Because, sir, I want to complete my education?'

'Couldn't you have completed it there?'

'No. I mean, I went as far as I could.'

'What do you want to be, a doctor?'

'No sir, my brother is studying to be a doctor at the University at Kyoto.'

This melted the doctor's gruffness somewhat. He looked thoughtfully at Kiyoshi.

4

'He is, is he?' the doctor said.

'Yes, sir,' Kiyoshi answered.

'Mm-mm. And you don't want to be a doctor?'

'Well ... it's not that I *don't want* to be one sir, it's ... Well I've never even thought about it.'

Again the silence from the older man. He was making his mind up about something. Then he said: 'I suppose I could ... what can you do?'

'I can't really *do* anything sir,' Kiyoshi said, 'but I'll learn quickly.'

'All right, you can start tomorrow morning at eight-thirty. Be punctual. I don't like latecomers. If you are any good, I'll keep you on to help me in the dispensary.'

Kiyoshi began to offer a profusion of thank-yous but the doctor cut him short. 'That's all right, I'm doing you no favours, you'll have to work hard for your money. By the way, before you go, what in fact are you going to study at these night classes?'

Kiyoshi told him, History, Geography, Mathematics and English. What he didn't tell him was that he was also going to comb the city for one of those places where Christians worshipped. He wanted to find out about this 'Man shall not live by bread alone' business.

He decided to see what these Christians did in their churches, and then perhaps he might meet somebody who would explain the strange sayings in the book called The Bible. It didn't take him long to find a Christian place of worship, and every Sunday for several weeks he slipped into the local Congregational Church. The ritual and the psalms and most of the talk only increased his puzzlement, and after his second visit he wrote to his brother:

'Dear Hidezi:

Ever since you brought home the book called The Bible, I have been trying very hard to find out what it means. Now that I am living in Kumamoto I am hoping to find someone

5

who will help me. Much of the book remains a mystery to me, but I find a strange peace each time I read it. However, for the past two weeks I have been attending a Congregational (what does that mean?) Church but am as far from a solution as ever....'

A few days later Hidezi's reply came. The letter was short and non-commital, but it did contain one bit of advice. 'I think it might be worth your while to search out the Lutheran pastor in Kumamoto,' Hidezi wrote. 'His name is Yamauchi. He may help you to understand this Bible thing.'

Kiyoshi Watanabe found the Lutheran church. Yes, the pastor's name *was* Yamauchi, and he would be very pleased to welcome Mr. Watanabe into his home and try to answer some of his questions. Kiyoshi had no intention of becoming too involved. After all, he was a Buddhist, as were all his family, but he would like to know the explanations of this Christianity business.

Little by little on successive visits to the Lutheran church, Kiyoshi was drawn towards this strange new religion. It meant, of course, the rejection of all he had ever been taught. The whole lot of Christianity was unfamiliar, often very difficult to comprehend. At the same time the deeper he got immersed in it, the stronger grew the sense of comfort he had felt when he first read the Bible.

Kiyoshi had to learn many new things; he had to cast aside the traditional Japanese scale of values which made the man in every family a far more important being than the mere wife; he learned what sin was, and why Christ had died. He learned about Christmas and Easter and about prayer, and he learned that he was now *bound* to love his fellow man. And all the time his knowledge of English increased. Firmly but gently the American missionary, Dr. Stirewald, refused to speak in Japanese during Bible classes. Thus Kiyoshi Watanabe learned all about his new religion in a foreign language until, in the end, he believed that Christ had talked in English also.

6

When Kiyoshi wrote to his parents and told them he was becoming a Christian, he wondered what their reaction would be. He need not have worried. His mother wrote back to him and gave him her blessing saying that she had no objection; neither had his father; their main concern was that he should be happy. This put the seal of happiness on his baptism, and in his joy he wrote to Hidezi in Kyoto and thanked him for being the first to introduce him to the Bible.

Less than a year passed before Kiyoshi finally made a definite decision about something which he had been considering for months on end. At last he was convinced that God had called him, and, renouncing any ideas of a civilian career, he entered the Theological Department of Kiushu Gakuin. It would be five long years before he would graduate as a Lutheran Pastor. Five years during which time Hidezi, by now a practising doctor in the family's home village of Nanataki, would help to pay the seminary fees. And yet Hidezi himself was unable to accept Christianity at all.

*   *   *

In 1915, when he was twenty-five years old, Kiyoshi Watanabe graduated in Theology, and his first clerical appointment was as Associate Pastor at the Lutheran Church in Omuta. At first he found the experience of preaching before a sea of gazing faces an awesome one—especially as those who sat before him were blank strangers. But gradually his confidence grew. When he was nervous he would say a quick prayer and ask for help, and at first when he did this he found himself contrasting Christianity with Buddhism. There was no doubt at all in his mind but that he had made the greatest decision in his young life on the day he had made up his mind to become a Christian.

As Rev. Watanabe grew fonder of his parish and parishioners, so one young lady of the congregation grew to love him. They became friendly, and in a very short time Kiyoshi knew he had met the girl who would be his wife. In 1916 he and Shigaru were married and a new era of great happiness began for them both. Daily Kiyoshi gave thanks for his marvellous good fortune, and when he learned that he and Shigaru were to be parents, he thought it impossible that his heart could contain all the joy he felt.

Strangely enough he discovered now that it didn't matter to him whether the child would be a boy or girl. He knew that as a Japanese he should be looking forward to a son for his first-born. It was traditional to be disappointed if the first-born turned out to be a girl. But Kiyoshi didn't mind. He was happy and contented, and boy or girl, the baby would be loved. The Watanabe's first child was a girl. A year later their second daughter was born. And after that came their first baby boy. He was called Shinya.

For seven years the family lived simply in Omuta. For Kiyoshi life could hold few new joys. All he wished for was that he would be spared for many more years so that he could serve Christ, and that he and Shigaru would be blessed with more children. Sometimes the family travelled back to Kiyoshi's home in Nanataki where proud grandparents played with and fondled the grandchildren. Kiyoshi and Hidezi talked as they had done when they were boys, and occasionally Kiyoshi tactfully asked the doctor-brother whether he had ever come any closer to an acceptance of Christianity. Always the answer was no.

There were times too when Kiyoshi wondered whether perhaps his father might become a Christian. But of course it was unthinkable that a son should ever even suggest that his father's religion was not the right one. Still, Kiyoshi hoped and prayed.

One evening when he came in from the church, it was a worried-looking Shigaru who met him. Before she even spoke he knew there was something radically wrong. He could hear the children wailing shrilly in their room. Then Shigaru started to cry.

8

'Oh Kiyoshi, it's our little girls, I don't know what to do.'
He tried to comfort her.

'Don't be alarmed, Shigaru. Tell me, what is wrong? Has there been an accident?'

His wife shook her head. 'No, no. I think it ... I think it's dysentery...' She couldn't go on, and though Kiyoshi tried hard to soothe her, he couldn't control the fear that was suddenly coursing through him. *Dysentery.* It was a dreaded word.

Presently he moved quietly into the room where his daughters lay tossing feverishly on their beds. Every now and then little moans escaped their lips. He went across, murmuring softly to them that soon they would be well again. But his voice did nothing to quieten them. He put his hands on their foreheads and felt the clammy heat of the fever. There was nothing he could do.

Two days later Kiyoshi Watanabe's two daughters, aged five and six were dead. His wife was distracted with grief, and Kiyoshi himself numb with the sense of loss. Why had this happened? Was there a wrong in his life, and was this...? But he cut short this questioning. God was omnipotent and all-understanding. The children had died because it was God's will that they should die. Kiyoshi humbly asked for both forgiveness and strength.

Little Shinya, the Watanabe's remaining child, pined for a while as he roamed through the house alone. Where there once had been gurgling laughter, there was now only the echo of a small voice. Kiyoshi and Shigaru often looked at the boy and hoped that soon he would have a new brother or sister to play with. Shigaru's quiet smile and coy look one day told Kiyoshi their wish was to be granted. So, God had taken two children, but now was about to give another in return.

The little girl, when she was born, was called Miwa.

Kiyoshi was again overjoyed. Now truly they were a real family once more; and when yet again Shigaru was to be a mother, Kiyoshi was convinced God was repaying in full the loss of the first two children.

9

Towards the end of Shigaru's pregnancy the doctor called Kiyoshi aside after one of the periodical medical check-ups.

'Mr. Watanabe, I'm bound to tell you that I'm worried about your wife's condition. She is not as well as she might be.'

Kiyoshi felt fear coursing through him again. 'What's wrong,' he asked the doctor. 'Is she going to lose the baby?'

'No, I don't think so. As far as I can tell the baby is all right. It's Mrs. Watanabe herself I'm worried about.'

Kiyoshi couldn't find anything to say. Alarm was making him wordless.

'Of course everything may be all right,' the doctor went on. 'I have no way of knowing for certain at this stage. But it is only right that you should know that complications are likely to arise.'

For a long time after the doctor left Kiyoshi sat sunk in depression. Obviously he would have to try to conceal his worry from Shigaru, but how was he to do it? Was there ever going to be an end to fear? Anyway, it was all in the hands of the Almighty. When Kiyoshi went back into Shigaru's room, he hoped his face would show no tell-tale signs.

After a long and difficult birth Kiyoshi's second son, Shigawo, was born. He was a beautiful child, and Kiyoshi and Shigaru often gazed at him in a sort of wonder. Kiyoshi, though, was worried. Shigaru wasn't recovering from the confinement as quickly as she should have been. Kiyoshi came frequently to the bed where she lay, tired and weak. When she smiled up at him, it was a pale smile, a sad thing.

And then one day Shigaru smiled no more. That was the day she died. Her little son was exactly nine days old. Her husband was heart broken.

CHAPTER II

The death of his wife left the young pastor in a terrible state. Shigaru, next to his religion and his God, had been his whole reason for living. Earlier, when his daughters died, he and Shigaru had turned to each other for comfort. But now there was no one to whom he could turn. And on top of that, he had a brand new baby to look after. Then, in the midst of his almost unbearable grief, he remembered the vows he made when he became a pastor; remembered that he had dedicated himself, body and soul, to Christ; remembered that he had decided to try always to accept totally the Divine Will.

The remembrance helped a little, but it could not completely assuage the frightful sense of loss and aloneness. And what about little Shigawo?

The idea of a man bringing up a newborn babe, nursing and feeding and changing it, was something that no self-respecting Japanese father would even let himself think about. Babies were womens' business. Certainly a father could love and be proud of his child—but bring it up? That was preposterous. The loss of face would be enough to make a man ashamed for the rest of his life.

So this was something else Kiyoshi had to wrestle with. Although all his instincts rebelled against it, in the end he took the hard way. For over a year he lavished all the care and attention he could on the baby. It was difficult, and many were the times he felt he couldn't go on. Yet always, somehow, he was

11

able to take care of the mite and at the same time not neglect his pastoral duties.

He was in Saga, in a new pastorship, when he met Mitsuko. She was a kindergarten teacher from his own town of Kumamoto, and she taught in Kurume from where she frequently came to attend Kiyoshi's church at Saga. As they both originally came from the same locality, they had a common topic of conversation, and the two made a point of seeking each other out each week after the services.

Mitsuko was a gentle creature who listened sympathetically while Kiyoshi talked to her about his problems. He in turn appreciated her gentleness and tact, and he found himself looking forward more and more to their meetings. When it dawned on him that he might be falling in love with this attractive girl, he tried desperately hard to put a brake on his emotions. After all, he reasoned to himself, I am a widower with three small children, and it would be palpably unfair to think of involving Mitsuko in someone like myself. Perhaps she would in time grow to love me, but have I any right to expect her to love my children? And besides, I am a full six years older than she is. And anyway, how do I know she will ever reciprocate my affection for her?

They were married very soon afterwards.

Mitsuko never seemed merely a step-mother to Kiyoshi's children. She loved them as if they were her own natural-born; Shinya and Shigawo and Miwa loved Mitsuko as their own mother; and Kiyoshi loved all of them with his whole being. Mitsuko he found to be as kind and understanding as Shigaru had been, and yet she was a completely different personality. He loved her for herself, for what she was and for what she meant to him.

Happiness in full measure had come back into Kiyoshi Watanabe's life.

*   *   *

12

Kiyoshi's sister, Sachiko, had gone to America as a young girl. There she married a young man who had emigrated originally from Nakashimi, a village close to her own Nanataki. Her husband, an industrious worker and astute businessman, made money from the seed business. Thus, when the 10th World Sunday School Convention was to be held in Los Angeles in 1928, Sachiko wrote to Kiyoshi inviting him to America and promising to pay all his expenses.

What Kiyoshi saw of the United States thrilled him. His three-month visit, during which he managed a coast-to-coast tour from San Diego to Seattle, passed very quickly; but not quickly enough to stop him longing to see Mitsuko and the children.

When he got back to Saga, he told his family about the wonderful new country he had been to; he told them about the great roaring cities and the huge highways carrying thousands of cars; he told them of the many friends he'd made, and he proudly demonstrated how much his English had improved.

Not long after arriving home he was transferred to Hiroshima, and there he stayed until 1935. The years were contented ones of domestic happiness and spiritual peace. The boys were growing up into healthy youngsters, and Miwa played the little mother to the two new baby sisters who arrived. Kiyoshi still went back occasionally to Nanataki, and on one such visit was amazed and very moved when his father called him aside and said: 'Kiyoshi, I have become a Christian.'

This was indeed wonderful news. Kiyoshi was lost for words and could only take his father's hand and press it warmly between his.

One day in 1935 a letter bearing American stamps and addressed to Kiyoshi arrived at the Watanabe home. What Kiyoshi read made him very excited. Then another feeling crept over him and fought with the excitement and finally overcame it and pushed it right out of Kiyoshi. Mitsuko, who could read her husband like a book, waited for a respectable time and then said: 'What is the matter Kiyoshi? You look worried.'

13

He thought long and deeply before replying. What should he say to her? Tell her the whole lot? That the letter was from his sister in America, and that she was now inviting him back again to America, and that this was to be no three month holiday, but a two year stay at the Theological Seminary at Gettysburg? Yes, he could tell her *that* all right. But how would he be able to...

He handed Mitsuko the letter.

'Mitsuko,' he said, 'this letter is from my sister. It delights me and worries me. But here, read it for yourself.'

There was a frown on Mitsuko's face as she flattened out the pages and began to read. The frown was still there when she stopped reading.

'I don't understand,' Mitsuko said, 'what is there in that to worry you?'

Kiyoshi went to her and held both her hands.

'I am worried,' he said, 'because of the invitation.'

Mitsuko laughed then, her most attractive laugh.

'I still don't understand,' she said. 'Don't you want to go?'

Kiyoshi dropped his head in a sort of embarrassment. This situation was slightly ridiculous, and for a moment he was inclined to doubt his wife's naïvete. However when he stole a quick glance at her, he saw she was playing no game; she was genuinely puzzled.

He said: 'Well, I *want* to go and I *don't* want to go. I want to go because it would be a great opportunity to learn more about Christianity. But I don't want to go for the reason that there is no mention of you, my wife. If I went, you and the children would have to stay behind. I think it is better if I decline my sister's offer.'

Mitsuko looked at him for many long seconds. No word passed between them, but her eyes held an expression of great tenderness. When she spoke, it was in a voice all softness, and yet with firmness underlining her words.

'You must not worry about us Kiyoshi. This is your life, and perhaps never again will an opportunity like this come your way. We shall be all right. And, if necessary, I can go back to teaching to earn some extra money.'

That was that. A few days later Kiyoshi applied to his church superiors, and these were pleased to recommend him for entry into the Gettysburg Seminary. Not only that—they also undertook to look after the financial welfare of Mitsuko and the children while he was away.

Came the day for him to leave. There were many tearful goodbyes from the family. Two years stretching out ahead like this seemed a very long time, and Mitsuko and Kiyoshi made each other promise that letters would be written regularly. Then, at last, he was leaving, and for a long time he waved. Even after the receding figures of his wife and family vanished from his view.

He sat back then and began to think. He was apprehensive about this visit to the U.S.A. Even though he welcomed the chance to study in a Western seminary, nevertheless he was experiencing more than a few qualms. Would his English stand up to the test? And how would people treat him? The last time he had come to the United States he had been only one of a very large party. But now he was to be on his own. He was unable to quell the shaking in his stomach.

* * *

It was a fine sunny afternoon the day he arrived at Gettysburg. Kiyoshi walked, almost apologetically, along the street from the station. He felt the strangeness and the atmosphere of this historic little town seeping into him. Suddenly three children darted out of a doorway and nearly bumped into him. Kiyoshi smiled tentatively at them.

One of the youngsters cocked his head perkily and said: 'Hullo' and then the other two said: 'Hullo!' and 'Hullo

15

Mister!' Then they ran down the pathway chasing each other in some childish game. In that moment Kiyoshi knew he was going to be happy in this town.

He walked on now with his head held up higher. The apprehension returned only when he reached the seminary, but immediately disappeared when he was welcomed in with warmth and hospitality. He was shown to his room, and when he opened the door and walked in he thought he'd made a mistake. There was someone else in the room already, a personable-looking young man lounging in a chair with his feet up on the desk in front of him. Kiyoshi was about to back out when the young man looked up.

'Hi John!' he bellowed, 'Come right in. I guess you 'n me are gonna be room-mates.'

Kiyoshi was surprised. He looked behind him to see who this John was. There was nobody there, and when he turned back the young man was hoisting himself out of the chair.

'Here John,' the young man was saying 'give me your bag and I'll stow it away.'

Kiyoshi smiled. So he himself was John? John, he repeated the name over in his head. Strange. He liked it. John Watanabe. It was a friendly-sounding name. Yes, he would like being John Watanabe.

He extended his hand to the American and said: 'I am very pleased to be here.'

'We're glad to have you. Make yourself at home.'

From that day on Kiyoshi was known as nothing else but John, and they put him on the receiving end of a brand of hospitality and kindness such as he had never before experienced. The next two years were to rank among the happiest (if at times the loneliest) of his entire life.

*   *   *

The Japan to which Kiyoshi Watanabe returned in 1937 was a far different place from the more-or-less peaceful country he had left in 1935. The first thing he noticed was that there were soldiers everywhere. Military trucks sped through the streets, and bustling men in uniform jostled the passersby on the pavements.

This was something new to Kiyoshi, and his first exhilaration at being home gave way to sensations of concern. He hated violence and war, and these soldiers represented those abhorrent things to him. Often, at the seminary in Gettysburg, there had been discussions about war. They always ended up by the groups unanimously agreeing that wars were useless, of no value and terrifyingly wasteful of human lives.

Once, one of the Americans had said: 'Suppose this country ever went to war with Japan, and we all had to go in the army, could you imagine having to go out there and take potshots at John! Could you? Why should I have to take a gun and go out there and kill somebody I don't even hate?'

The others laughed, but only briefly. They became serious then and said, well, old John was some one they'd never shoot at.

Kiyoshi was thinking of all this just outside Hiroshima station when someone suddenly touched his elbow. He turned, and there was little Kimi grinning up at him. Nearby, Mitsuko was standing with Kei and Miwa. Mitsuko's eyes were full and, as usual when Kiyoshi and she were feeling emotional, they both just stood there, quite still, staring at each other for several silent seconds. Their eyes did the talking.

Back in their own home, after the excitement of distributing the presents from America, and once the children were settled for a while, Kiyoshi asked Mitsuko to come and walk with him. Together they strolled through the Hiroshima streets. He was home again, and Kiyoshi was looking for changes. But, apart from the military uniforms everywhere, there were no changes. The same shops stood in the same positions. The buildings were just as shabby or just as smart, and the streets twisted and

17

turned in just the same spots. Places he had passed hundreds of times before he now stopped and gazed at and drank in. They went into Asano Park and in the quietness underneath the trees, Kiyoshi stopped once and kissed his wife slowly and very softly. It was as if he were seeing her for the first time and didn't want to miss a single detail. They walked on in silence until they reached Sakai bridge, and there he threw a little twig down into the water and watched it float away. And on Misasa bridge Mitsuko did the same thing. Their hands found each other.

Kiyoshi turned to Mitsuko and talked very quietly.

'I've missed you, Mitsuko. I've missed you very much.'

She looked straight at his eyes.

'I've missed you too, Kiyoshi, more, much more than I can tell you. It's ... it's *good* to have you home again.'

There didn't seem to be any more to say. Anything else would have broken the spell. They walked a long way after that in a deeply happy silence. Each knew the wonder of the other's company after such a long time apart.

In the weeks and months that followed, Kiyoshi became very conscious of the increase in military movement. The news from Europe was ominous, and though Germany and Poland were thousands of miles across the other side of the world, Kiyoshi still felt a stab of real fear when at last the news of September 3rd 1939 flashed into Japan.

He knelt that night and prayed that the war in Europe would soon end: 'Please dear God, let the madness that afflicts them soon depart. Let the bloodshed stop so that men may live in peace once more and do Thy Holy Will. And, most of all dear Lord, preserve my family and my beloved country from the horrors of war.'

As the newspapers screamed their headlines and the wireless blared out new accounts of the carnage in Europe, dark rumours spread through Japan. Sometimes Kiyoshi looked around at his family and quaked inside at the thought of them ever becoming the victims of war; and yet each day seemed to be bringing Japan ever closer to it. The circumstances seemed to be marshalling themselves towards the point where the clash would be inevitable. Kiyoshi prayed continually for peace, but, to him, the military and the politicians seemed bent on warfare.

Towards the end even the churches suffered, and after the oppression which followed the efforts to unite all denominations into a controlled Christian sect, Rev. Watanabe's church in Hiroshima was closed. He couldn't understand half of what was going on. His mind and brain were unable to cope with the subtleties and intrigues of power politics. He didn't know why countries *had* to be belligerent instead of doing their utmost to avert the explosion.

After his church closed, he applied for and got a job as a teacher at Kiushu Jo Gakuin in Kumamoto. There he was set to teaching English to girls between the ages of fifteen and nineteen. Meanwhile, in Hiroshima, Mitsuko was Headmistress of the Good Samaritan Kindergarten School in Takasho Street. Two teachers in the same family! Kiyoshi occasionally playfully chided Mitsuko about the fact that he had never received any training, and yet here he was teaching—and doing quite nicely.

It was in September 1941 that Kiyoshi went to Kiushu Jo Gakuin. Three months later the announcement that Pearl Harbour had been attacked by the Japanese blazed through Japan. Everywhere people shouted for joy in the streets, the newspapers and newscasters became hysterical and incoherent, and Kiyoshi Watanabe was happy that Japan, if she *had* to fight, had started into the war with such a tremendous impact.

All young men of twenty were conscripted. Many there were who didn't even wait to be called up, but went immediately they were eligible, and volunteered. Militarism took over completely, and each day brought its news of fresh Japanese victories. At Kiushu Jo Gakuin even the girls donned uniforms and learned to march like soldiers. Kiyoshi watched them and felt good inside that these too loved their country as he did.

Shinya and Shigawo were called up, and Kiyoshi's heart swelled when he saw his sons looking so fine in their uniforms.

19

When they went away he made them promise to remember the spirit of Bushido—the Kight-like code of honour of ancient Japan—their prayers, and their mother and father.

And then one day a letter in a War Department envelope arrived addressed to himself. Surely at his age they weren't calling him up? They were—but not as a soldier. He was to report without delay to Tokyo where he would be officially signed on as a civilian interpreter attached to the Army.

Even though he had been only three months at the school, Kiyoshi had become one of the most popular teachers there. On the day he left, the girls who formed his classes lined up to bid him goodbye. They cheered as he waved farewell, and as he moved away, it was to the repeated call of 'Banzai! Banzai!' It was a good feeling to be seen off like this.

Leaving home wasn't as easy. Mitsuko cried uncontrollably on Hiroshima station, and the last view he had of her was with her face streaming with tears, her body shaken by uncontrollable sobs. Then she was lost from sight, and, his own last reserves of control exhausted, Kiyoshi sat back and covered his face with his hands.

CHAPTER III

The February day in 1942 on which the transport carrying Kiyoshi Watanabe nosed her way through Lyemun Gap and into the harbour of Hong Kong, was crisp and clear. There was a distinct bite to the breeze which blew along the deck and Kiyoshi was shivering slightly. He moved away from the starboard side and crossed through the staterooms and out on to the promenade deck on the other side. It was less windy here, so he took the few steps which brought him to the rail and got his first view of Hong Kong.

What he saw took his breath away. He had never seen such a beautiful sight before. Across the water from him he could see the sprawling city of Victoria dipping its toes into the sea. High above it The Peak, a tiny fringe of wispy cloud at the top, looked down in immobile grandeur. Dotted about the sides of the hills were what one man was later to describe as 'villas drowned in gardens', and stately mansions which nestled cosily into the niches which had been hewn for them out of the rock-face.

As the ship glided slowly towards the mooring buoys, Kiyoshi was able to distinguish the thousands of bright clean Rising Sun flags fluttering from every available flagpole on the island. The sight made his heart leap; that so many proud emblems of his country's success should be in evidence seemed to him oddly like a special welcome. His one regret was that Mitsuko could not be

21

here with him to see the beauty of this place, and to share the chest-swelling pride he felt for the splendid Japanese army.

Later, when the launch came to take him ashore, he nearly fell down the gangway in his eagerness to walk in this conquered city which soon would be a permanent part of Japan. Perhaps then, some day, he would bring Mitsuko and the children here and say: 'Look, this is Hong Kong—which some say means Fragrant Harbour—and I was here two short months after our victorious army first made it the property of our country.'

It was only when he landed that he first noticed the other things—the shattered buildings and the mounds of rubble, the charred jagged ends of protruding timber beams. There was an air of depression and of surly resentment in the streets, and when he passed some Chinese coolies and looked straight into their faces, they turned away. There was something in their eyes which spelt hatred.

Everywhere Japanese soldiers were swaggering proudly, even arrogantly, elbowing the Chinese and Portuguese out of the way. This seemed a little unnecessary to Kiyoshi, but he supposed it was because of the pride which is said to change men when they win victories over their adversaries. A little of this pride rubbed off onto himself, and he squared his shoulders and pretended he was a real soldier and not just an interpreter. However, barely seconds later he was put to the test. When an old Chinese woman heavily laden with bundles of rags came towards him along the path, he instinctively stepped aside to let her pass.

Immediately there was a burst of sardonic laughter from across the road. He looked up to see four or five Japanese in military uniforms pointing at him.

One of them shouted: 'You fool! *Don't* get off the footpath for these damned Chinese. Make *them* get into the gutter where they belong. Remember you are a *Japanese*! Be proud of it!'

Then the soldiers walked away, half angry, half amused.

There was a vague uneasiness gnawing at Kiyoshi and it took him some while to dismiss it. Could it be that he was becoming too sensitive in his old age? He realised with a pang that he was fifty-two—at least he would be, on the fourteenth of next month. Still, he *felt* young, and that was the main thing.

He reported at the Hong Kong Headquarters where they told him that, as an interpreter, he should take himself to the Headquarters of the Prison Camp Administration on the Kowloon side. When he walked out of the building and into the afternoon sunlight, he wasn't feeling like a soldier any more. The people in the H.Q. used the word 'interpreter' with an emphasis that betrayed, only too clearly, their cynical attitude towards 'these civilians in uniform'.

Kiyoshi spent the next ten minutes fighting his way through the queues who were waiting for the ferry to take them across the harbour. Kowloon was built on the peninsula that jutted out from the Chinese mainland into the bay of Hong Kong. On the way across Kiyoshi remembered something that he had heard back in Japan. A man at the depot had said: 'Interpreters? The interpreter comes well down the list. First in importance comes the soldier; next his horse, and only then the interpreter.' The truth of this theory was now making itself felt on Kiyoshi. For a second or two he even allowed himself a few regrets. If only he might wake up soon and find that all this army and war business were only a bad dream, and that he was really at home in his bed in Hiroshima. If only...

The gentle bumping of the ferry as she came alongside the pier startled him out of his day-dreaming. When he stepped ashore in Kowloon the sight of the bright Japanese flags fluttering right along to where the huge bulk of the Peninsula Hotel marked the start of Nathan Road again quickened his spirits.

In the building in Prince Edward Road which was being used as the Prison Camps Administration Headquarters, Interpreter Watanabe came face to face with Colonel Tokunaga, commandant of all prison camps in the island. The colonel, an immaculately dressed and precise man from whose every gesture

23

one could read 'career soldier', was brief, barely courteous and to the point.

'Mr. Watanabe,' he said, 'welcome to Hong Kong. I hope you will like it here. I am appointing you to Shamshui Po prison camp where you will take up your duties as interpreter as from tomorrow morning. Although you are not a real soldier, I shall expect you to dress and behave according to the best traditions of the army. That is all.'

Tokunaga turned away abruptly and picked up some papers off his desk. Undecided what to do—he didn't quite know whether the colonel had dismissed him or not—Kiyoshi Watanabe stayed where he was. Tokunaga looked up again and shouted: 'Well, what are you waiting for? I said that was all, didn't I?'

The little interpreter bowed low and said: 'Yes, sir. I am sorry. Thank you, sir.'

The soldier who led him to the bus stop walked straight to the head of the queue of people standing there waiting. When the bus arrived, the soldier pushed Kiyoshi aboard and then disappeared back towards the H.Q.

Inside the bus, the Chinese passengers were all standing, huddled together in the gangway. A thin sprinkling of Japanese soldiers were occupying the seats, one soldier to each seat designed for two people. These men were sitting with their legs spread wide and their swords held in front of them. To Kiyoshi this behaviour was laughable, so when the Chinese in some miraculous way melted back to let him pass, he sat in the one empty seat and pushed himself right in close to the window. Nobody sat in the vacant space. Not even when he turned and indicated it. He was ignored.

At the end of the ride Kiyoshi followed the soldiers off the bus. He picked up his luggage and went in past the Police Station towards the gates. Straight ahead he saw the barbed wire entanglements, and beyond, holding the strands and looking mutely outwards, several hundred men. Once, when he set down his cases in order to rest his hands, he looked back over his shoulder to see what the prisoners were staring at. Against the fronts of the houses he saw them, the women. Some were crying softly into handkerchiefs; others trying desperately hard to smile, and yet others rocking backwards and forwards in that motion which, in any land, denotes extreme grief.

There was a great silence all over the place apart from the crying of the women. Every now and then one of the armed sentries shouted a coarse obscenity at them. Kiyoshi winced. It was some consolation to know that most of the women would not understand the Japanese tongue. The things that were shouted were loathsome.

After reporting to the office just inside the camp gates, Kiyoshi was shown to his quarters. He was tired now, and after a wash and a change of clothing, he lay back on his bed and rested.

His thoughts turned naturally towards home. He wondered what Mitsuko would be doing at this precise moment. He thought about Shinya and Shigawo, his two sons, who were away somewhere in the army. He thought about Miwa, his eldest daughter, and about the two 'babies', Kimi and Kei.

Presently he slept.

CHAPTER IV

Kiyoshi Watanabe didn't know where he was. He lay quite still trying to puzzle it out. The window wasn't in its usual place. Neither was the door. In these first waking moments he was caught in the half-world between dreams and reality. In fact the greater part of his mind was still linked with the dream he had just come out of, and he could still hear the little snatches of conversation between himself and Mitsuko and Kimi and Kei.

Gradually, as the sleep left him, recognition of his surroundings came back. Of course—he was in Hong Kong, and he was no longer the Reverend Kiyoshi Watanabe, Lutheran pastor. No, he was Interpreter Watanabe K., Imperial Japanese Army.

He got out of bed and the coldness of the February morning hit him. As he got dressed and washed he wondered what the day would bring. When the Chinese boy came in carrying two pairs of boots which had been shined to gleaming, Kiyoshi tried English on him.

'I do not speak Chinese. Do you understand English?'

'Yes, sir. I speak. I many year work English officer. Now I work you.'

Kiyoshi smiled back at him. Well, at least they would be able to communicate fairly successfully with each other.

After a light breakfast in his room he thought he would take a look at this place where he was to work. He slipped away and walked out towards the seafront, past Jubilee Buildings. He looked across the harbour from which the morning mist was just rising. The ferries were criss-crossing in and out amongst the sampans. The junks, with their frail-looking batwing sails, looked like elegant high-sterned models. There was an atmosphere of peace for a short time. The scene was one of rare beauty. Kiyoshi swept his eyes in a clear arc round from the Peak until he was gazing at Stonecutters Island, lying like a huge somnolent whale not far from where he was standing. He could feel the peace and the beauty at this moment, and though it was only for a moment, he knew it was his, all of it.

Then a Japanese voice barked harshly somewhere in behind him, and within seconds the air was filled with the sounds of the camp being roused. He turned his back on the sea and walked straight in towards the camp office. He didn't know at all what to expect. Having been a civilian for his entire fifty-two years, and a pastor for most of it, he had no idea what duties the army would find for him. He was a stranger here and knew nobody. He would have admitted that he felt more than a little odd in uniform.

The camp commandant, when he met him, turned out to be a tall slim young lieutenant who dismissed him curtly.

'My name is Lieutenant Sakaino,' the officer said. 'You will work at first in the camp office. You will see from the others what you are expected to do. You may go.'

In the camp office Kiyoshi Watanabe introduced himself to the other interpreters. He was received coolly, and he was very much aware that the others were sizing him up. During the rest of the morning he familiarised himself with the various papers that were in use; after lunch he was set to filling in forms. Am I going to be nothing more than a form-filler? he asked himself. Is this all I am—a clerk? I had hoped to be something better than just that. And I want to *see* these prisoners, the men beaten into submission by our army. I want to see these British soldiers and sailors and airmen.

The opportunity came the very next morning when he had to go on first roll-call. Before he went out he felt the excitement of

27

exultation in his belly. He knew this wasn't a wholesome feeling, especially for someone like himself, a Minister of God. Such people should learn to control their base feelings. But, after all, he reasoned, I *am* a man, and I suppose it is natural for me to have instincts. I am proud only because I am Japanese, one of the victors, and I am about to stand before the vanquished.

When he got nearer the lines of men for his first look at them, the exultation left him and it was replaced by something far more sobering, even sickening. Looked at from behind, the men (how many are there? he wondered; there must be *thousands*) appeared to be in appalling condition. Their clothes were ragged and dirty. Many were only half dressed, and a lot of bodies were thin and emaciated.

When he walked round to the front of them and saw their faces he was appalled. Here were men whose human dignity had been taken from them. He looked at the haggard faces and ripped and torn clothing, and he felt pity beginning to well up inside him.

He tried hard to rationalise this thing, this peculiar emotion that was tearing at him. These men in front of him, they had fought and been beaten. They were his stated enemies, the enemies of Japan. Therefore they were not deserving of pity. Theoretically anyway. They had to pay the penalty for losing. Someone had to be the loser. If it hadn't been the British, it would have been the Japanese, and with the boot on the other foot, would the British have expended any pity on their prisoners of war? War is war, he thought, and I must not be soft. It behoves me to be stern, steadfast—because I am one of the conquerors. I am Japanese. I love Japan.

But there was still this thing inside him, despite all the reasoning and the arguing. It still stayed there. Before the day's work in the office really started in earnest he spoke to Inouye, one of the other interpreters, about it.

'I feel a little stupid about admitting this,' Watanabe said, 'but when I first went out there on roll-call this morning, I couldn't help feeling sorry for all those men, those prisoners.'

Inouye dropped his pen and walked across to him.

'Did you say you felt sorry?' Inouye asked.

'Yes, I ... it was something involuntary. I have never seen prisoners of war before. It came as a shock to me to see their condition.'

'I don't understand you,' Inouye said, and his voice was strangely and ominously quiet.

'Well, it's just that I don't know *what* I expected to see,' Watanabe went on. 'But it wasn't what I did see. Those men looked half-starved and sick. Is this right? Let me explain it this way: You see I spent some time in America, 1935 to 1937, and that was my main contact with Western people as a mass. I found them dignified and well-ordered and content. And they were so friendly. But those out there...'

'My dear Watanabe your pity is misplaced. Pity *them*! It serves the pigs right. They are treated far too well for my liking, but then I hate them. All of them. I *hate* them.'

The Christian and the pastor in Kiyoshi recoiled at this word 'hate'. This was the first time he had ever heard a man use it about other human beings and really mean it. He had to say something about it now, but all that came out was an embarrassed laugh and an apologetic: 'I don't think it is necessary to *hate* anyone.'

'Well, I hate them, and so should every good Japanese. What's wrong with you, Watanabe? Is it that you are *not* a good Japanese?'

Kiyoshi Watanabe was frightened. He was also indignant. He was frightened at the sight of someone so consumed with hatred. He was indignant that anyone should doubt that he, Kiyoshi Watanabe, was a good Japanese. He was proud of and loyal to his country. His mind fought for words to say to Inouye, but the words remained unvoiced. Inouye's eyes narrowed and took on a faraway look as if he was remembering.

Then he said: 'Yes, I shall get my revenge, every single day and night's worth. I shall treat them like the filthy animals they are and deserve to be.'

29

'That is not the way of God,' Kiyoshi said, and he said it without thinking, involuntarily, because it was an instinctive thing for him to say.

Inouye bent down to him.

'God? So you are a Christian, are you?'

'Yes,' Kiyoshi said, 'I am a Christian.' He picked up his pen and began to write something, anything, on the piece of paper in front of him. Other people, the remainder of the office staff, were coming in. He wished Inouye would go away now and leave him alone. He was sorry he had started the conversation, and just hoped against hope Inouye would let the matter drop. But Inouye stayed sitting on the table.

Inouye said, after a little while: 'Let me tell you this, Mr. Christian Watanabe, I too have lived amongst them, in Canada, and they despised me. I knew it. I could feel it. They humiliated me. I was just another dirty little Jap to them. But two can play that game, and now they are the pigs and I am the master. The pendulum always swings the other way too. It has already been their way, now it has come to my side.'

Inouye left when he saw that Watanabe was not going to be drawn any further into this conversation. For two whole hours Kiyoshi sat unseeing at his desk. He was thinking about this awful hate which was seething in his fellow interpreter. This wasn't typical of all Japanese. But was this going to be the face of Japan which the whole world would grow to know?

'Watanabe!'

He looked up. Inouye was standing near the open door leading to the camp commandant's office.

'The commandant wishes you to be present at the questioning of a prisoner,' Inouye said, then turned on his heel and walked away.

Kiyoshi got up and went in to the commandant's office, arriving there just before a young Britisher was marched in. The boy couldn't have been more than twenty, and his face was quite impassive when the charge against him was rattled out in Japanese. When the NCO finished, Inouye translated and told

30

the Britisher he was being accused of trying to steal some rice. The charge was emphatically denied, and Kiyoshi caught a glimpse of Inouye striding across the room towards the prisoner. Inouye swung his arm and punched the young Britisher full in the mouth, making the blood spurt bright red on his chin.

'The charge is *true*, you *did* try to steal rice, didn't you?' Inouye shrieked. His voice had gone higher into an ugly high-pitched tone.

Again the British soldier denied the charge against him. This time Inouye slapped him hard across the face, first with the palm of his hand, then with the back of his knuckles as he brought his hand back in a vicious arc.

Kiyoshi Watanabe felt himself becoming sick, but he turned his eyes down to his feet so that he didn't have to watch what was going on. When he did look up it was Inouye's face he looked at. Inouye was wearing a thin smile of malice as he beat the Britisher. When the face-slapping and the punching failed to produce the desired admission, Inouye turned to Sakaino.

'Sir,' he said, 'may I take him away for some further questioning?'

Sakaino nodded, and the Britisher was half dragged, half shoved into a nearby room.

Inouye called over his shoulder: 'Come in here, Watanabe and see our persuasion. We must get the truth from these Englishmen. Come, you'll be doing this yourself soon.'

Kiyoshi Watanabe followed with a heavy heart. His legs felt weak and rubbery, and he thought he was going to faint. He loved true things, and he knew that Inouye's use of the word 'truth' was no more than a mockery.

When the Britisher got the belt buckle across the naked chest the first time and moaned from the agony of it, Kiyoshi could stand it no longer. He ran from the room, into the lavatory and bolted the door behind him. In there he attempted to close his eyes and ears from the horror. Then he was sick—with shame and revulsion and despair.

He took out his handkerchief and buried his mouth in it to

deaden the sounds of the sobs that were tearing him. Oh God, was this what war did to men? Was it for this that Christ, the Son of God, became Man and died on a cross? Watanabe could find no answer, and in his black despair he wondered if he wasn't losing his mind. Worse, he wondered if he wasn't losing his faith in God.

He got down on his knees in the confined and smelling space and prayed until the words became more than mere repeated sounds, until they started to mean something, until they began to blot out the scenes and the doubts, until he was actually talking to his God and pleading desperately for help. He asked for many things—strength and help and understanding. And faith.

He finished by saying: 'Forgive me Father, forgive me for my weakness and frailty. Forgive Inouye his cruelty even as Thou forgave the thief on the Cross. And take me, unworthy and frail as I am, and do with me what You will. Make me the tool of Thy goodness. Not my will, but Thy will be done.'

He knelt in reverence and humility. When he stood up a calmness was already flowing into his veins, and with it an as yet undefined determination. The future, he knew, was going to be hard. He would have to walk carefully, risk his life, perhaps even lose it. But the only thing he feared was physical pain. I am a coward, he told himself, I am a coward and I am afraid of pain. I am a coward, O God, so please help me.

As he slipped back the bolt and walked out again into the sunlight, he had the certainty of knowing that no matter what he did or suffered, he would be watched over by Him to whom he had just offered his life.

*   *   *

For a few days after the beating incident, Watanabe kept to

himself. The reaction to what he had seen hadn't set in properly yet, and indeed it was twenty-four hours before the full brunt of it hit him. When it did, it was in the form of a staggering attack on his mental faculties and sensitivities. Then all the thoughts and emotions which made a turmoil of his mind precipitated him into a state of confusion in which he was afraid to speak. He did not want a repetition of the Inouye business, though he knew full well that at some time or other in the future he might have to face far worse. There were other conflicts which had to be solved too. He asked himself a thousand times if his instinctive desire to help the prisoners of war wasn't traitorous. Japan, his mother country, was very dear to him, and he loved her far too much ever to entertain any real thoughts of treason.

But, during the long nights, and up to the grey hours before dawn, he lay sleepless, his mind a torment. At the end of each day he felt exhausted, and yet too tensed up to sleep. Questions whirled maddeningly inside his head until he craved a few brief hours' sleep as respite. He wished Mitsuko were near at hand so that he could tell her the things that worried him; dear gentle Mitsuko who could listen so patiently and often resolve his problems in her own quiet simple fashion.

But Mitsuko was far away in Hiroshima, oblivious of Kiyoshi's mental stresses. When he wrote to her, as he did often, he never mentioned what he had found in Hong Kong, nor what the discovery was doing to him. Instead he told her of the beauty of the place and described painstakingly the simpler things in his life, like what food he was eating, what the weather was like and the condition in which his shirts came back from the laundry.

Writing these simple letters to his wife was for him like going into rare little oases where misery was unknown. At each writing he prized his consciousness away from the happenings and thoughts which distressed him. He projected himself into the atmosphere of his home at Takasho Street, and asked simple searching questions about Kimi and Kei. He enquired about the older children also, Miwa and the two boys Shinya and Shigawo.

But once the letters were written, and their answers read, his mind once more seethed with doubts and fears and total confusion. And then, after a period of mental anguish, the soul-searching crystallised out into a clear-cut question. The facts stood out startlingly clear to him, ranged as they were on opposite sides. What was it to be—God or Country?

For Kiyoshi Watanabe there could be only one answer to that. He made his decision. 'For the least you do unto one of these, my children, you do also unto me.' The words he knew so well, and quoted so often, would be his guide from now on. Furthermore, there would be no need to reject any of his loyalty to Japan. He would merely try, in his own small way, to ease the lot of the hungry, the diseased and the dying. In other words, he would endeavour to remain a human being.

The day he made his decision he walked more briskly than he had done for days. On his way to the office in the afternoon he had to squeeze past two British officers who unwittingly barred his path. He bowed slightly in his natural respectful way, smiled and said: 'Excuse me.' The officers stood aside, surprise written all over their faces.

Two minutes later, in the interpreters' office, Inouye came at him, eyes blazing.

'Watanabe, I should have you knocked down! When I heard you saying "Excuse me" to those Britishers I wanted to punch your face. There is no need to be polite to them. If I ever hear it from you again you will be sorry.'

Kiyoshi said nothing, but on the inside he glowed a little and thought, this is the beginning; already I feel a little better.

There were times when his senses reeled at what he saw in the camp area. Wasted skeletons of men who were ravaged by dysentery, hundreds of others reduced to a worse than poor physical condition through lack of food, horrifying sights which made him wonder to what further depths his country—or to be more correct, his country's army—could descend. His heart was

34

filled with compassion, and he wondered if his puny efforts to right even a minute fraction of the wrongs would serve any purpose at all. When this sort of thinking inserted itself into the receptive corners of his mind, he fought it viciously, tried with all his power to evict it because he knew it would undermine the whole structure of his new determination.

He got himself into the habit of praying much more often than previously he had been accustomed to. Not that he had ever been particularly drawn to formal prayer. He preferred instead to hold conversations with God during which he would repeatedly ask for help for himself and for others. Mealtimes he found particularly appropriate for this form of prayer, because it was at such periods when he was thanking the Almighty for His goodness, that to ask for some further aid seemed more than natural.

One Sunday morning, when he was off duty, he heard singing in the camp. He left his room and went out to try and find the source. This was no ordinary burst of song. He thought he detected a reverence in the sound. Within seconds he was on the edge of a huge crowd of men who were standing, heads bare, facing a booming-voiced chaplain who was balancing precariously on a chair. Kiyoshi stood on the verge and listened, and wished with all his might that he could join in the service. Here was proof beyond all doubt that no matter what hardships or brutality men had to suffer, they need never forget their God. He stood unobserved, and he looked around the faces. Young faces and old faces, they were all suffused with a seriousness which brought a warm hotness to his eyes. These men, from the Western world with all its differences, were standing on this Sunday morning, paying homage to the same Jesus Christ that he himself adored.

When the singing stopped the padre, a captain, spoke a short sermon which Kiyoshi listened to and partially understood. He was looking intently at the British clergyman when he felt the eyes of those prisoners nearest him looking his way. He was in two minds as to what to do. If he moved away now they might

35

construe his presence as an act of snooping; on the other hand he felt he had hardly any real right to stay at what was after all a private gathering.

In the end he moved away from the spot where he had been standing and edged around as unobtrusively as possible until he was not far from where the army padre was. He folded his hands and stood, eyes downcast, listening to the words of hope. When the flow of speech stopped he looked up just in time to see the padre turning away. So, the padre had seen him too? Well, there was no point in creeping away like a whipped cur now, so he stood his ground and breathed a sigh of relief when the padre commenced talking again. When the sermon was over, a short prayer was said in which the prisoner congregation were asked to repeat the words the padre said. Kiyoshi closed his eyes, and though he did not speak the words aloud, he repeated them all in his mind. In this way he felt he had taken part in the service. He felt genuine regret when the crowd of men started to break away. Many of them, in passing close to him, stared hard at him, and made no attempt to hide their annoyance at his presence.

'Excuse me!'

It was the padre's voice, and Kiyoshi turned to see the captain walking towards him.

'My name is Davies,' the captain was saying. 'I saw you listening to my sermon. You are not a Christian by any chance?'

'Yes, I am a Christian,' Kiyoshi answered. He was pleased to see there was no obvious dislike showing on the other's face. 'I am also a minister, a pastor, like you.'

Padre Davies cocked his head sideways and looked quizzically at Kiyoshi. 'You don't say! What denomination are you then?'

'Lutheran,' the interpreter answered.

'Well I'll be blowed!' Padre Davies said. 'I didn't think there was a single Japanese Christian in the camp.'

'I think I'm the only one,' Kiyoshi said. 'Thank you for letting me listen to your sermon.'

'There's no need to thank *me*,' Davies said. 'I mean *you* can go wherever you like in this camp, you have the right, your people are the bosses, we're the prisoners.'

'I didn't mean that,' Kiyoshi said. 'You might have considered me an intruder and kept quiet until I moved away. But you didn't do that—you carried on with your service. I am grateful.'

'Oh now look, for goodness sake!' the padre said, 'I mean you're a Christian, I'm a Christian, that's what Christianity is, isn't it? If it isn't, we've all got hold of the wrong end of things. Look I'm very glad to know that you're a Christian. At least in *that* respect we look in the same direction.'

The two men, made enemies by war but whose shared faith in Christianity had somehow transcended the barriers, talked together for a long time in the compound.

A week later, at Padre Davies's next service, Kiyoshi came again and this time stood close to the Welshman, passively taking part in the adoration of their common God.

The meeting, and what he subsequently found out, was to affect Davies so profoundly that eighteen years later, when preaching in St. Martins In The Fields in the heart of London, he would base his sermon on the Christianity of Kiyoshi Watanabe, the Japanese interpreter from the prison camp of Shamshui Po.

CHAPTER V

The women that Kiyoshi saw outside the camp the day he arrived, came every day and stood in the same place, looking at the men behind the wire. Some brought parcels which were addressed with the names of prisoners, parcels which at first were rejected by the camp commandant. In time however, he relented, and a weekly 'parcels day' was instituted. On such days the women came, each holding her precious package of food for her husband or father or son.

The interpreters were detailed off as examiners and stood, like customs officers, behind examination tables to which the parcels were brought and searched. Kiyoshi saw some of his fellow interpreters going to the length of cutting open tomatoes 'to make sure nothing was hidden away in them'. This he considered ridiculous and needlessly harsh. He could see no point in being so officious, and his parcel examination was far less severe than that of the other examiners.

The women were quick to notice this, and as time went by the word spread among them until eventually, on parcels day, long queues formed in front of his table. At the other tables, mere handfuls of women stood waiting.

Inevitably Watanabe was called before Sakaino. The lieutenant ranted and swore at him and said he was not severe enough.

During the tirade, Watanabe stood, letting the words run off him. He wasn't really listening. He stood with his ears mentally blocked, and he couldn't help wondering why all this shouting had to go on just because he had let an occasional harmless bottle of beer slip through unchallenged. Little things like that were hardly going to defeat Japan. They were of no moment.

Sakaino was finishing, shouting as loudly as ever.

'...and all the other examiners are indignant, Watanabe. Do you understand? So from now on I am taking you off parcels inspection. I warn you, from now on you are going to be watched.'

So, in future he was going to be watched, was he? Well, he'd have to be more careful. He considered what the best course of action would be, and decided to stay quiet until the stir he had caused died down a little.

The other interpreters didn't appear to want to talk to him, except to abuse him. They avoided any friendly conversation with him, though both Matsudo and Sekiguchi had originally impressed him as being decent enough types. Matsudo spoke English with a pronounced Welsh accent, picked up before the war when he lived and worked for a time in Wales. Sekiguchi once said he *had* been a Christian.

It took Kiyoshi quite a while to realise that a lot of the dislike for himself was conditioned by a fear they all had of the Chief Interpreter, a man named Nimori. Nimori held the rank of lieutenant and was in charge of all the prison camp interpreters. His quick temper and enormous personal vanity made him a man to beware of. He seemed to have a consuming hatred of all things and people Western. Kiyoshi felt that the other interpreters were afraid that Nimori would think less of them for associating with someone who was considered unnecessarily soft towards the P.O.W.'s.

Sometimes, when they passed close to each other, Watanabe and padre Davies exchanged smiles of recognition. Then one day Watanabe noticed that the Welshman wasn't around any more. He checked the office files and discovered that the padre had in fact been temporarily moved to St. Theresa's Hospital. He felt a sense of loss at the other's going. Although they never held conversations with each other after the first one, he had come to look upon Davies as a friend.

However, the knowledge that one of the interpreters was a Christian, in civilian life a minister of religion, must have been passed around, because soon Kiyoshi Watanabe found he had a new friend—this time a Roman Catholic priest. The latter explained his dire need of sacred vestments to the Japanese. Kiyoshi listened sympathetically and promised to see what he could do about it.

Sakaino's face was a mask of disdain when Watanabe asked if the commandant would permit sacred vestments for the Catholic priest to be brought into the camp. When permission was eventually grudgingly granted, the interpreter made his way to the Catholic Church the priest had mentioned. There he explained the needs of the prisoner. He was welcomed inside by an Irish father who went away to collect the vestments.

Kiyoshi looked, full of curiosity, at the, to him, strange garments, and when he tentatively asked if the priest would tell him what they were and what they represented, the Irishman gladly began to tell him. He picked them up one by one. 'First the *Amice*, a square of white cloth put on over the shoulders with the prayer that it will be, for its wearer, "a helmet of salvation"; next the *Alb*, the long white linen garment which calls from the priest the hope that he "may be cleansed and made white in the Blood of the Lamb"; then the symbol of holy purity—a heavy cord of silk named the *Cincture*.

'And then this is called the *Maniple*, a band of coloured cloth worn over the left forearm like this. The idea beind it is that it should remind the celebrant of the Mass that in gathering fruits for Almighty God, he must fear neither labour nor suffering.'

Kiyoshi hardly listened to what was said about the *Stole* and the *Chasuble*. What the priest had said about *not fearing labour nor suffering* had struck home with him.

Going back into the camp he received many inquisitive looks from the sentries and the other interpreters. But this time there was no fear in him. He walked straight into the camp commandant's office, planked the huge bulky parcel on the desk and said: 'These are the vestments for the Roman Catholic padre, sir.'

'Take this muck with you too, Watanabe!' he shouted and and dismissed him.

Sakaino snorted some deprecatory remark about Christianity pushed the parcel of vestments off the desk and on to the floor.

The gratitude of the Catholic padre, when Kiyoshi handed him the vestments, was self-evident. It made the derision of Sakaino worthwhile bearing. There would be so much too to write to Mitsuko about Catholicism. What a pity, he thought, that all Christians do not resolve their differences and come together. After all, the same God is worshipped by all the various denominations. If only ... if only ...

He was still thinking about it a few days later in the camp office. He was alone, except for a Japanese clerk who knew no English. The door was knocked on, and then opened to reveal a petite young woman in her mid 'twenties who was talking even before she was announced. Within seconds Kiyoshi elicited the information that she wanted to see the camp commandant, that she was the mother of three young children, that both her husband and her father, who had been members of the Hong Kong Volunteer Defence Corps, were now prisoners in the camp, that she wanted to see them too, and that she had lived in Shanghai for many years before the war.

All this came out in an unstoppable rush of words in which English and occasional Japanese phrases were inextricably mixed up. And the English was heavily laced with American idioms and phrases which he thought she had probably picked up in Shanghai where so many Americans had lived in the old days. Kiyoshi had never heard so many words spoken in such a short time before, and torrents more were still coming at him. The woman was a peculiar mixture of deference and audacity, and while the words were pouring over him, the interpreter could feel an idea taking root in his mind. By the time the woman left him, he was already thinking that perhaps here was a very useful contact for him on the outside. Perhaps through her he would be able to do something really valuable to help the men in the camp. Before she left, he got her address from her and said he would try to call on her soon.

Already minor outbreaks of disease had appeared in the camp. There were ominous whispers about the likelihood of an epidemic. Kiyoshi had seen what beri-beri could do to people, and now that many of the prisoners were complaining of sore throats, there was a general fear that diphtheria might break out. He knew of the repeated requests from the camp doctors for serum. He knew too of the refusals.

Well, maybe this woman—what was her name again? She had said her name was Nellie Lee—maybe somehow she would be able to organise something on the outside. Then he, as someone who had more-or-less freedom to come and go as he pleased, would be of some real use.

Working six days a week, he knew that the only opportunity he would have of visiting this Nellie Lee would be on Sunday. On the few days still to run before week's end, he gave the matter a lot of thought. Gradually another picture merged with his vision of Nellie Lee the helper—he began to think of her as somebody who also *needed* help. He recognised in this woman, now alone with three children, a parallel to Mitsuko, alone in Japan with her family. Both were women whose husbands had been taken away from them.

The food position in the Colony was bad, and any that could be bought was only on sale on the Black Market. And at exorbitant prices. Therefore a woman like Nellie must be in a bad way now that her source of income was cut off. Therefore her children would go hungry. Therefore he, Kiyoshi Watanabe, must obviously do his best to help them.

From then on, at meals, he made a point of trying to save

42

portions of any dish he thought would keep without going rotten. It meant lingering at the table until everyone else was finished, or else trying to slip the tit-bits unobserved into his pocket.

Once the sharp-eyed Inouye noticed and said loudly: 'What are you up to, Watanabe? Feeding pet mice in your room?'

Everybody laughed, including Kiyoshi. That was the last time he tried taking the food that way. Anyway, by then, he had a *feruski* almost full of food, mostly Japanese rice cake, hanging up in his room.

On the Sunday he walked out of the camp wearing uniform. He didn't bother to check whether or not he was being followed. It was natural for the camp office staff to come and go as they pleased on a Sunday. It was their one day off.

As well as this, many of them had their own Chinese women fixed up already. Those who hadn't, freelanced, dropping in at any of the many houses which advertised, quite brazenly in Cantonese, 'Finest Kind of Girls Here'. Kiyoshi reasoned that anyone seeing him going in to a house would naturally assume he too was either fixed up, or about to be!

At the door of the flat he was met by the same mercurial young woman who had come to the camp office earlier in the week.

'Why, it's Mr. Watanabe!' she exclaimed. 'How nice of you to come. Come on in and meet my children.'

Thinking that the children might be afraid when they saw someone in a Japanese uniform, he hung back.

'Are you sure it will be all right?' he asked.

'Yes, sure, of course it will. Look, tell me your name. What'll I call you?'

He said: 'My name is Kiyoshi—Kiyoshi Watanabe.'

'Well they'll never get their tongues around that one for a start!' she said.

The rapidity of her speech and the colloquialism puzzled him.

'I am sorry,' he said, 'I do not understand.'

43

'Your name—they won't be able to say it. It's too difficult, too hard to say. Haven't you got a simpler name?'

His mind flashed back to a day seven years ago, to the day he walked into his room at the Gettysburg seminary for the first time. He remembered the way the American boy greeted him.

'My English name is—John,' he told Nellie Lee.

She grabbed him by the arm then and hauled him inside.

'Come on,' she said. Then, 'Kids ... Junie, Wendy, Barbie! Come and meet Uncle John.'

Three young girls emerged from a door across the room and ran towards him. They were saying: 'Hello Uncle John, Hello Uncle John.'

He picked up the smallest one, and she came into his arms willingly, full of uninhibited friendliness. This was a good feeling. He knew straight away that the little girl and her sisters must be missing their father. He wondered if he himself might not be able, in however vague a way, to partially make up for their father's absence from their lives.

'You know, Uncle John, it's kind of funny having a Japanese army man in here. Not funny really, it kind of scares me.'

'But I'm not really an army man, Mrs. Lee. I am an interpreter.'

'Oh don't call me Mrs. Lee, it makes me sound so old. Call me Nellie.'

'Very well Mrs. Lee, I will call you Nellie!'

They both laughed at that.

'No, but really what I was getting at, I don't want to insult you or anything, but some of the things your soldiers have been doing to our people are unbelievable. You know, I mean war is war, sure, but jeepers the Japanese have been making Hong Kong people hate them since they arrived here. And here I am with a man in Japanese uniform playing with my kids. It's eerie, that's what.'

Kiyoshi had his head bent low as he tickled one of the little girls into gales of laughter. Everything that this Nellie Lee had

44

said about his people was uncomfortably true. He daren't look her straight in the face. She would see the shame in his expression. The shame and the hurt. He kept his eyes averted from her.

'You don't have to be afraid of *me*,' was all he said.

'Tickle me, tickle me! Please Uncle John, tickle me!' Junie shouted. 'Uncle John.' It sounded so trusting and so natural.

'Uncle John,' Nellie Lee said, coming towards him and putting her hand tentatively on his arm. 'Uncle John, know something? I'm not, I'm not afraid of you at all.'

A lump came into his throat. When he raised his eyes, he knew they were glistening. 'Thank you,' he said. 'Thank you for not being afraid. And thank you for my new name—Uncle John.'

The three children joined hands and formed a dancing circle around him, and they chanted the name over and over again. 'Uncle John. Uncle John. Uncle John.' He stood in the middle, embarrassed and happy. And Nellie Lee stood laughing delightedly at her Junie, Wendy and Barbie.

Later Uncle John (that's how he thought of himself now) was mentally calculating how much money he could afford to give to their mother each month from his pay. His allowance to Mitsuko swallowed most of what the army gave him. What was left for himself was little more than pocket money. But this woman needed money far worse than he.

He felt quite at home with the children, and they played naturally with him. When the time came for him to leave he felt sorry. He wasn't looking forward to returning to the inhospitable prison camp with its misery and its suspicious personnel. Nellie had talked to him of her husband, and had asked if he would pass on some verbal messages to him, and also to her father. She had also spoken of her desire to help some of the thousands of men who had no relatives to send in parcels to them. Other than that she made no mention of enlisting Uncle John's help. However, the idea that had prompted him to visit ner in the first instance was stronger than ever in him as he said

45

goodbye to Nellie and the children and made his way back to Shamshui Po.

*   *   *

During the week he contacted Nellie's husband and father and passed on the messages Nellie had asked him to deliver. There was no mistaking the pleasure the men got from receiving direct news from the outside. Uncle John could see immediately the boost other men's morale would get if they too could receive similar messages. This was something he would have to mention to Nellie the next time he saw her.

On the following Sunday he decided to chance going out in civilian clothes. Strictly speaking it was against regulations. He was supposed to wear uniform. But most of the others seemed to disregard this regulation about wearing uniform at all times in public. He would not be so conspicuous in a lounge suit, and anybody who saw him making tracks for the flat might mistake him for a Japanese civilian who was resident in Hong Kong before the war.

He reached Nellie Lee's place without being apprehended and the children welcomed him warmly. They evidently had adopted him as their new Uncle without any reservations at all. They crowded around him, dancing with excitement when he put the *feruski* down in front of him and started to untie it. There were loud 'ooh's' and 'ah's' while he drew out the choice morsels so carefully put away during the week.

Meanwhile Nellie hovered around, occasionally correcting their manners. She was very proud of them.

'Now now children! Give Uncle John a chance! June! Don't be rude, you know you're supposed to be an example to your young sisters. Oh, Uncle John, you *shouldn't*! I bet you went hungry yourself so that you could bring all those lovely things to us.'

46

Kiyoshi Watanabe felt embarrassed when she said things like this. He just laughed and said: 'It is nothing.'

He thought about the naturalness with which they all referred to him as Uncle John. It sounded so real—as if he was already accepted as one of the family. He was happier than he had been for a long time.

When the children went to bed, Uncle John told Nellie that he had talked to her husband and father, and that they were keeping well and sent their love. Her eyes had tears in them when she heard this. Uncle John knew it was as much from happiness and gratitude as from sadness.

He stayed with her as long as he dared, but he had to be back in the camp by a certain hour. When he was leaving, Nellie gave him a list of messages for the husbands of other women who had contacted her. Uncle John promised to do the best he could. Then he said goodnight and stepped briskly out into the street. He walked for a long time before getting on a bus.

* * *

'Uncle John, I'd like you to meet a friend of mine the next time you come. Is that all right?'

It was two weeks later. Nellie looked anxious as she asked the question. Uncle John couldn't make out why.

'Yes of course, if you like,' he said.

'Oh good. He is an Englishman, a doctor. Doctor Selwyn-Clarke.'

A small doubt crossed Uncle John's mind. An English doctor. That was odd. He thought all English civilians had been interned in Stanley Camp on Hong Kong island.

'When do you wish me to meet this Doctor Selwyn-Clarke?' he asked.

'Next week if you'll be here,' Nellie said. 'Will you be coming next Sunday?'

47

'Yes, I hope so.'

'Fine. That's settled then. Now, tell me, what have you been doing with yourself this week, eh?'

For a couple of hours they sat and talked. She asked him all about his life in Japan before the war, got him to describe his home and his family to her. He told her he was a Christian, and asked her if she was one. Yes, she said, she too was a Christian.

'Then there is something special I want you to do for me,' he said. 'I want you to pray for me. You and Junie and Barbie and Wendy. Will you do that?'

She nodded.

'Thank you. I shall also pray for you, every day.'

On his way back to the camp he became depressed again. During the past few weeks the health condition of the prisoners had deteriorated rapidly. Any time he walked around now, and indeed every morning at roll-call, he saw men who were losing their sight and walking awkwardly because of what beri-beri was doing to them. He thought, what a terrible sight to see the men looking like this. The sight of vast numbers of ill prisoners upset him. He felt it was beyond his ability to help them. On one occasion, when he was alone, he had burst out with: 'God, how can You allow this to happen?' That was one of the main reasons he had asked Nellie to pray for him—so that he would not feel like that again. It would be so wrong.

Now, sitting on the bus, he was thinking of this Doctor Selwyn-Clarke. The name meant nothing to him. But a doctor might be able to do something, anything, to ease the misery of the sick men. There was nothing definite in his mind, just a hope. It made him feel a little better though, and he was almost cheerful again by the time he reached the camp gates. He was looking forward to Sunday.

*   *   *

48

The children had been packed off somewhere by the time Uncle John arrived at Nellie's flat a week later. Only Nellie herself was there, and she was looking pretty in a bright dress. While she was preparing something in another room, he sat and tried to conjure up some idea of what this English doctor would look like. He had nothing to go on. All Nellie had told him was that he was an Englishman and that he was a doctor.

At the ring on the doorbell, Nellie flurried out from the other room and fairly skimmed across to the front door.

'That will be him?' he said.

A tall man with grey hair stepped into the flat.

'Doctor Selwyn-Clarke, I want you to meet my Japanese friend, Uncle John Watanabe. Uncle John, this is Doctor Selwyn-Clarke.'

Uncle John bowed slightly, and the doctor extended a hand.

It was a very soft English voice which said: 'How do you do, Mr. Watanabe. Mrs. Lee has been telling me a lot about you.'

Nellie said: 'Oh don't call him Mr. Watanabe, you'll embarrass him. Call him Uncle John. He'd much rather be called Uncle John, wouldn't you, Uncle John?"

Uncle John was embarrassed already.

He said: 'Yes please, whatever you wish.'

'Very well then,' Selwyn-Clarke said, 'Uncle John it shall be.'

Nellie and the doctor talked too fast when speaking to each other for Uncle John to be able to understand more than half of what they were saying. However, he felt that Nellie was going too far when she said: 'Uncle John here is absolutely wonderful. He's been a marvellous help. I don't know what the kids or I would do only for him. They simply adore him. Don't they, Uncle John?'

A few times he felt Selwyn-Clarke's eyes on him, sizing him up in much the same way as he had been sized up the day he arrived at Shamshui Po. Whenever he looked straight at Selwyn-Clarke, the doctor tactfully glanced away. All through the afternoon Uncle John wanted to offer to do *anything* the doctor might ask if it meant that the suffering of those in the camp might be eased in any way. But he thought it tactful to remain silent. If Nellie wanted to, she could tell Selwyn-Clarke. Perhaps she had done so already.

Uncle John thought Selwyn-Clarke must be the typical English gentleman. His courtesy had a grace about it that Uncle John had only ever read about. The Japanese sat and watched and spoke little. His admiration of the English doctor grew.

When Selwyn-Clarke left, he shook hands with Uncle John once more and said: 'It has been a great pleasure meeting you Mister—Uncle John I mean. I hope we shall meet again soon. Au revoir.'

When the door had closed behind him, Nellie came back in smiling.

'Well Uncle John! Did you like him? Isn't he wonderful?' she said.

'Yes,' Uncle John said. 'A perfect English gentleman, that is what I think he is.'

'Oh I think he's just great. He is a very prominent man. But I can't tell you any more about that just now. Maybe later, huh?'

'Nellie,' Uncle John said, 'if you and your friend Doctor Selwyn-Clarke want me to help you, you know I will do it. Please tell him that.'

'You bet I will, and Uncle John ... thanks a lot.'

They spent the remainder of the evening talking about the war. She asked him how things were in the camp, and when he told her of the spread of the sickness, alarm showed on her face. He reassured her and said her husband and father were both all right, that the food they got in her weekly parcels had helped to build up a resistance to sickness. Then she asked about the other men, the ones she knew or knew about. She wanted the news to pass on to the relatives.

When she gave him more of her opinions about some of the things the Japanese soldiers had done in the Colony, he felt ashamed again. He could make no explanations, because he himself didn't know why these things were done. She hinted at the barbarity of the Kempeitai—the Japanese military police. But she wasn't telling him anything he didn't know. He had heard all about the finger-nail pulling and the water treatment. He too had seen some of it—the men struck in the face with rifle butts, and those on punishment who had been made to kneel for hours bare-legged on sharp edges of wood. These were things he tried hard to forget.

* * *

The diphtheria which scythed through the camp met very little resistance. There was a pitifully small quantity of serum which, within hours, was completely used. From then on those who contracted the disease lay down with it, reached their crises, and either died or pulled through. Many died. Sometimes it reached a figure of seven or eight in a day, and a man who might be on a burial party on a Tuesday could well be dead himself by Thursday.

For Uncle John it was a wretched time. There was no opportunity for him to attend a funeral, and in the camp office he often sat and brooded about the sadness of the men who died so very far from their native country. He prayed for them. It was all he could do. He hoped that the doctor he had met at Nellie's would be able to suggest something. Sunday was a long time coming.

When it did come, for once he had little time for the children. They were hurt when Uncle John was offhand with them. He couldn't help that. He was worried and had to talk to their mother about the serious state of affairs in the camp. Nellie cleared the children out of the room when she saw Uncle John's expression.

'Nellie,' he began, 'you know that friend of yours, Doctor Selwyn-Clarke?'

'Yes,' she said, 'and I want to talk to you about him later. But go on, what is it you want to ask?'

'The camp, Nellie—things are very bad. The diphtheria you understand, many men are dying. I was wondering if your friend could do anything, if I could be of any help.'

'That's what I wanted to talk to *you* about! But first, Frank and my father—are they all right?'

Uncle John nodded.

'Yes, thank God,' he said, 'they are all right so far. But there are many others who are not.'

'Right, well now you listen to me for a moment, Uncle John. I wanted you to meet Dr. Selwyn-Clarke for a specific reason. In actual fact I wanted *him* to meet you. You remember you said you would help in any way you could? Well I'd an idea early on that perhaps through you we could establish a means of getting certain necessities into the camp. I mentioned this to Dr. Selwyn-Clarke, and of course at first he wasn't sure about it. I suggested that he come here and meet you. That way he could make up his own mind about you. During this last week I saw him again, and he was very impressed by you, he said. Oh, and incidentally, he asked me to convey to you his kindest regards. He also said he would be deeply grateful if you would do something very special on behalf of the prisoners.'

Uncle John said: 'Anything Nellie, anything at all I am capable of.'

She said: 'Bless you, I knew that would be your answer. Well, this is the plan, if it is possible for you to carry it out...'

She went on then to explain to him that Selwyn-Clarke had gathered together a small pack of surgical instruments and various other medical equipment, including some of the precious serum for diphtheria inoculations. If these could be smuggled into the camp, no doubt a number of lives could be saved. But whoever carried the stuff in, would be doing it at great personal risk.

From the other room she brought out a canework case which she put on the table and opened for him. Inside, carefully packed, were the gleaming instruments, scalpels and knives and syringes.

'Do you think you can manage to get them in, Uncle John?' Nellie asked.

'Yes, I think so,' he said. 'But I shall have to go soon, because there is a special time in the afternoon, around now, when there is very little movement in the camp. The sentries relax somewhat, and I don't think they would take very much notice of me.'

'How do you intend getting this lot past them?' she asked.

'I will carry it in that case and walk straight in.'

'And if they stop you?'

'I do not think they will. I am not afraid. But I must go now. If you will get the children to say a prayer for me, I will be all right.'

'Of course I will, Uncle John.' She pressed his hand in a gesture of thanks. 'Goodbye, and God bless you.'

The case was heavy and seemed to get heavier the farther he walked. He changed it from hand to hand to rest his arms. In the end he had to stop and put the case with its invaluable contents on the ground. After a little rest he walked on again. As he neared the camp gates he became increasingly nervous. It was important that he should carry this through successfully, but it wasn't easy when you feared the Kempeitai as he feared them.

Several times, on the last stretch, Japanese soldiers coming the opposite way glanced at him and then at his case. One of them passed a remark to his companion which brought a shout of laughter. Uncle John was scared whenever this happened. It would attract attention to him that he couldn't afford.

And then he was at the gates. As he had guessed, it was a slack time. The sentries gave him no more than a few glances of vague curiosity, and then he was inside. Now would be the trickiest part. As he walked further away from the men at the gate, he wanted to look behind him to see if they were watching him. To do so would draw suspicion on himself. At the same

53

time he had to keep a sharp watch to see if any of the officers were about, because it was they would would be most likely to stop him and ask him what he was carrying in the case. He plodded on towards the hut where he slept. Any second he expected a shout. The tension got worse step by step, and the case felt heavier every inch of the way.

He reached his room at last and pushed the case under the bed, pulling the sheet well down so as to hide it from sight. The nervous tension and the exertion of carrying the case had taken their toll of him. He threw off his jacket and flopped into a chair. The worst part was over. He now only had to find the man to whom the stuff was to be delivered. What was his name?

There was a moment of panic when he couldn't call the name to mind, but then he remembered Nellie pushing a piece of paper into his jacket pocket with the name written on it. He smoothed out the paper and read the name. It said: 'Dr. Ashton-Rose, Indian Medical Service.'

Under a pretext of getting some documents that he needed, he went into the office later on when dusk was settling over the camp. As quickly as possible he picked out the record sheets and hunted through the names until he found Ashton-Rose's name, and opposite it his hut number. Uncle John waited in his own room then until the camp was almost in darkness.

Nervousness was tearing at his innards as he made his way through the lines of huts. Carrying the case like this was highly dangerous. It would take only the curiosity of a guard to put him in a terrifying position. Uncle John trembled, despised himself for the cowardice that made him react like this, and pushed his feet on and on over the darkened ground.

Ashton-Rose, when he found him, was uncommunicative. Uncle John didn't blame him. The whole set-up must have appeared highly dangerous to the doctor—being searched out like this in the darkness; being confronted by an enemy; being asked for identification. Uncle John was in a hurry. He handed the heavy case to Ashton-Rose.

'From Dr. Selwyn-Clarke,' Uncle John said. 'And please, would you give me a receipt.'

Ashton-Rose momentarily hesitated. Somewhere outside in the night there was the sound of a sentry's footsteps. Uncle John could feel his heart thumping with panic.

'Please, will you hurry,' he said.

Ashton-Rose flicked open the instrument case, allowed his eyes to widen in amazement, and then hurriedly scrawled a receipt for Uncle John. He grabbed Uncle John's hand with both of his own and squeezed very tightly. Then he slipped away into the shadows leaving Uncle John to pick his way back to his hut.

Uncle John rounded the edge of a block of buildings just as a sentry was passing out of sight. The man heard something and stopped. Uncle John froze, bit hard on his thumb to suppress his chattering teeth and stood immobile for what seemed like hours before the sentry finally carried on walking.

When he reached his room, Uncle John collapsed on his bed. He went into a dead faint, and when he came to was violently sick on the floor.

CHAPTER VI

During July and August 1942 I was out of Shamshui Po Camp, acting as Chaplain to St. Theresa's Hospital. While I was there I noticed a lot of fellows coming in with sore throats. It took me a long time to realise what it was all about—diphtheria had broken out. When St. Theresa's closed I went back into Shamshui Po, and that was when I got the biggest shock I received during the entire war. I was horrified. Dysentery was rampant, morale was at rock bottom, and fellows I had seen fit and well only a few weeks before, were now hobbling around like old men—walking skeletons.

One of the awful things was that we had no idea at all of how the war was going. There was this sense of being completely cut off. The place was in desperate need of medical supplies and men were dying every day. Then we heard that one of the interpreters, a Christian named Watanabe, had begun to smuggle in serum to some of our own camp doctors. He was doing this at great danger to himself, but you see though he was a loyal Japanese, he retained all his Christian principles AND LIVED BY THEM.

Rev. H. L. O. Davies,
(formerly chaplain to the
Middlesex Regiment in Hong Kong.)

*   *   *

56

It was two weeks after handing over the case to Ashton-Rose that Uncle John again saw Dr. Selwyn-Clarke. But in the interim period there was a chilling summons into the presence of Chief Interpreter Nimori.

Nimori called him into the commandant's empty office, Sakaino having gone to Headquarters for a conference with Colonel Tokunaga.

'So you are Mr. Watanabe,' Nimori began. 'Let me tell you straight away, I don't like you. They tell me you are a Christian. Is Buddhism not good enough for you? No, I suppose you have to ape the Westerners in religion as well as in everything else.'

He turned his back on Uncle John. Uncle John wondered what was coming next. There didn't seem any point in saying anything. What could he say? It was useless denying that he was a Christian—records had all the information on him written down.

Nimori was standing looking out of the window towards the centre of the compound. Without turning round he said:

'Our proud enemy don't look so proud any more, do they, Watanabe?'

Uncle John remained silent.

Nimori said: 'I asked you a question Mr. Watanabe. The proud British are not so proud now, eh?'

Uncle John said: 'No sir, they are not.'

'I am told, Watanabe, that you feel sympathetic towards them. Is that correct?'

Uncle John could not deny that either. He said: 'Yes, I feel sorry for those who are sick and hungry.'

Nimori turned around and faced him. 'You know the penalty for helping the enemy, don't you? It is a capital crime, and the punishment is death. You understand that, don't you?'

Uncle John said, quietly: 'Yes, I understand.'

'Very well then,' Nimori said, 'that is all.'

Uncle John left the room and went back and sat at his own desk. He could feel the eyes of the others on him, and it was an

57

uncomfortable feeling. He sat for over an hour staring at the forms in front of him. He was unable to think. He wondered if somebody had learned about the medical supplies, and, that night, when writing to Mitsuko, he could barely keep his mind on what he was doing.

The next few days were uncomfortable ones during which he waited by the hour for a summons to Sakaino's office. When it didn't come by the end of the week, he knew the first smuggling-in had been a success after all. Nimori's interview with its thinly veiled threats must have been no more than coincidental. Uncle John thanked God for seeing him through and hoped this was only the first of many such episodes.

On the Saturday morning Interpreters Matsudo and Seki-guchi were off duty and Uncle John was informed that he would be required to do some interpreting that afternoon. Some prisoners were due to appear before the camp commandant on charges of breach of discipline. This sort of assignment was one of those things Uncle John had been dreading ever since the day he had seen Inouye beating the soldier with a belt buckle.

Accordingly, when the first of the men was marched in Uncle John stood on one side feeling extremely nervous. The charge was rattled off in Japanese which he translated into English for the prisoner's benefit. There was the inevitable denial.

'What does he say?' Sakaino snapped.

'He denies the charge sir,' Uncle John said. He was finding it hard to control his voice.

'Is he calling the Japanese liars?' Sakaino was shouting.

Uncle John translated this for the British soldier who said he was not calling anybody a liar, but that he was not guilty of the charge against him. When Uncle John passed the answer to Sakaino, the officer thumped the desk angrily.

'What are you standing there for, Watanabe? Get the truth out of him! What have you got hands for?'

Uncle John did not move.

'Watanabe! Are you going to stand there and let him get away with it?'

Sakaino was on his feet and coming around from behind his desk. He said: 'Hit him!'

Uncle John could not do it.

Sakaino slapped the Britisher across the mouth with his open palm.

'Like *that*, Watanabe,' he said. He motioned to the guards who promptly pushed the charged soldier out of the door towards the room where Inouye had done his 'investigation'.

'Now,' Sakaino was saying, 'in there and get the truth out of him, and quickly. Get it any way you can, but be quick.'

Still Uncle John could not bring himself to do what Sakaino expected him to do. He stood his ground, looking at his feet, feeling the sweat wetting his hands.

Sakaino continued to shout at him, until Uncle John feared the other might have a seizure from the apoplexy which was making him tremble. He would have to say *something*, because it was his silence which was driving Sakaino crazy.

'Sir, I cannot do it. I cannot beat a man.'

The effect of this on Sakaino was terrifying. The commandant lost all vestiges of control, and he became incoherent. He kept on screaming: 'You are a great fool, you are useless, a fool! Get out! You foolish old man! You are useless!'

Uncle John's only hope was that the prisoner wouldn't suffer an increased punishment because of him. Sakaino, in a rage, was liable to do anything.

*   *   *

At Nellie's flat on the following day, Uncle John kept to himself the events of the past few days. No good could be done by telling her. In any event she had enough troubles of her own without worrying about his. Nellie asked him if he had delivered the equipment.

He held up the basket to her and let the lid hang open.

'There, you see, it is empty. I have come back for more.

She laughed and fussed around him saying he was great and wonderful and marvellous. He wished she wouldn't talk like this.

'It is *nothing*, Nellie, nothing. I am only trying something very small.'

'Oh go on with you !' she laughed. 'I think you're terrific, and that's all about it.'

He asked her if Selwyn-Clarke was coming, and was delighted when she said Yes, she hoped so. While waiting for the doctor, he got down and played with the children. They seemed glad that Uncle John was back to his old cheery self again, and that the stern worried-looking man of a few weeks back was no longer in evidence. Nellie shot her customary questions about Frank and her father, and Uncle John gave her the little news he had been able to get. She asked him too about conditions in the camp, but as the children were present, he warded off the question and changed the subject.

He was very pleased when Selwyn-Clarke called him Uncle John as soon as he came in.

The doctor walked towards him with his hand outstretched and said: 'Ah, my dear Uncle John, how good to see you.'

They exchanged formalities, and then Uncle John took out the slip of paper bearing Ashton-Rose's signature and gave it to Selwyn-Clarke.

Uncle John said: 'There, a receipt to prove I delivered the equipment as promised.'

'You don't have to prove anything to me, Uncle John,' Selwyn-Clarke said. 'I trusted you implicitly.'

Uncle John bowed at the compliment, but the other man went on talking.

'I want you to know how grateful I am, and indeed how grateful we all are, Uncle John, for what you have done. This will not go unforgotten. I am fully aware of the risks involved, and of the worry you must have suffered before coming to your decision to help what are, after all, enemies of your country. I know that what you are doing in no way affects your loyalty to Japan. I wouldn't dream of ever trying to interfere with this loyalty, so believe me that as a doctor I know the humanitarianism which prompts you to do what you are doing.'

Uncle John was very touched by what Selwyn-Clarke said. It was amazing how a near-stranger could understand so fully the things which had gone through his head. He admired too the doctor's appreciation of his feelings towards Japan. Selwyn-Clarke, he felt, must be one of the finest human beings he had met.

Over a meal he told the doctor about how heavy the case was, and how he had had to put it down several times in order to rest his arms.

'Poor Uncle John,' Selwyn-Clarke laughed, 'well, we shall have to do something about that. Leave it to me. I think perhaps I can get you a more convenient carrier.'

He did too, and the next consignment of medicine and instruments were carried by Uncle John in a fine leather brief-case provided by Selwyn-Clarke.*

*   *   *

On one day alone, seventeen men died of dysentery and diphtheria combined. There was no serum in the camp, and the medical treatment was very rough and ready. We knew that someone did bring a quantity of serum to the camp gate—but it was thrown on the ground in front of the P.O.W.'s and smashed by one of the guards. Later on I know that one of the civilian interpreters did in fact smuggle a small quantity of serum

---

* Uncle John kept this briefcase right through the war until the end of hostilities. After that it went back to Japan with him and in 1960 he still had it, worn out and ragged.

into the camp, and this was used to treat the worst cases.

Subsequently the little camp hospital managed to get more medicines of all sorts, but (as one of the seven officers in the O.R.'s camp) I knew that these had to be kept hidden from the Japanese M.O.

I knew that the Japanese interpreter was the main source of supply, and that he was regarded as being very different from the rest of them. He also brought messages from friends who were not themselves interned, and made a genuine effort to help us. He was one of the few Japanese who could be approached without fear of reprisals. Where he got his supplies was not known, but it was obviously from a friendly source, and it was NOT *Japanese issue.*

Lieutenant Colonel G. C. E. Crew, RASC.
(based on the war diary he kept whilst
imprisoned in Shamshui Po)

Each time he went for a new supply of medicines and medical equipment, Uncle John wondered if the fear he experienced would ever lessen. He thought that after making two or three trips into the camp with the forbidden supplies he might become used to it. But it did not turn out that way. Whenever he got off the bus and started the last part of the journey on foot, the fear came back to him. It made his stomach feel weak and trembly, and his throat went dry. He couldn't banish from his mind the things the Kempeitai did to people. Death, of itself, held no terrors for him. What appalled him was the prospect that he might be tortured. He held physical pain in great dread.

What made it harder was having to conceal his fear from Nellie and the doctor. It wouldn't do to let the woman know that he was afraid; to admit to the British doctor that a member of the Japanese forces, though only an interpreter, was capable of fear, would mean a terrible loss of face. In front of these two he always contrived to be cheerful, as if the taking of risks was something he had been accustomed to all his life.

These days he found it much easier to pray, because now he

was earnestly asking for something which he was convinced only God could provide—protection. And besides, there was his promise to Nellie that he would pray for her and the three children. He was convinced that it was the prayers of the children which alone kept him out of trouble. Like the time 'the miracle' happened.

He had got off the bus as usual, and for once the approach to the camp was completely deserted. He was relieved that this time at least his task would be relatively easy. The sentries now rarely took more than a mild interest in him, and when he was passing he made a point of suiting his manner to those who were on duty. Some of them liked to be recognised and spoken to. To these he was affable. Others were surly and resented any approach being made to them. With these Uncle John remained quiet and slipped in and out of the gates with a minimum of fuss. By now he knew the characteristics of every man who was on the guard roster.

The most hazardous part of the smuggling trips was the period between the time he actually got inside the gates and the moment that he was safely inside his own room. That was when he was most likely to be stopped by an inquisitive officer or N.C.O. who might ask what he was carrying. So far this had not happened to him. He could hardly believe his good luck.

This time, however, he was no sooner past the sentries than coming towards him he saw a sergeant who had only been in the camp a short time. He was an officious little man who poked his nose into everyone's business. Uncle John's heart dropped when he saw him. He pretended not to have noticed, and tried to veer off out of the other man's path.

'Mr. Watanabe!'

Uncle John felt his legs going weak at the sound of the sergeant's voice.

'Good afternoon, sergeant,' he said.

The N.C.O. swaggered towards him, his hand resting on the handle of his samurai sword to prevent it from swinging.

'That is a fine brief-case you are carrying. What have you got in it?'

Uncle John didn't know what to answer. He tried to say: 'Nothing,' but his voice wouldn't work.

The sergeant put out his hand for the brief-case and said: 'Show, let me see.'

Uncle John dumbly handed the case to him. There was a great confusion of thought in his head, and he was unable to think clearly. The sergeant was fumbling at the catch of the case.

'Heavy, isn't it? What's inside?'

Still Uncle John was unable to talk. He didn't know at all what he would say when the sergeant got the case open and found what was inside. So he just stood, petrified with fear, incapable of thinking up an excuse.

Then the catch clicked and the sergeant lifted the cover and looked inside.

Uncle John expected him to go berserk with anger and to start shouting. He would scream things like 'Traitor! You are betraying Japan! Traitor!'

The sergeant did not speak a word. He merely closed the case again and walked away.

Uncle John went back to his room, pushed the case under his bed and waited for the consequences. Nothing happened, either that evening or the next day or any day afterwards. By rights the sergeant should have reported the matter to the camp commandant immediately and Uncle John should have been placed under arrest. But no mention was made about the incident ever again. Uncle John was convinced that the fact he was not reported and charged was a miracle. A miracle he attributed to the power of the prayers of Nellie Lee's three children.

He was nearly a whole week late delivering that consignment, and he could sense the alarm its failure to arrive was causing amongst the camp doctors. But he couldn't take the risk of moving too soon in case the sergeant was biding his time to see who the receiver was.

64

It wasn't necessary to get a receipt for the medicines any more, though when Selwyn-Clarke occasionally sent in monetary funds, he asked for signatures. This, he explained to Uncle John, was only so that records could be kept straight.

Gradually the numbers dying from diphtheria became fewer; the epidemic was checked, finally controlled. But there would be many trips yet before it was stamped out completely. All the time Uncle John knew he was being watched. He mentioned this to Nellie after a while, because by now he had learned who Selwyn-Clarke really was.

Nellie had only hinted at it early on when she said he was a doctor and a very prominent man. In fact he had been, before the Japanese occupation, Director of Medical Services for the Colony of Hong Kong. That he was still free was more than surprising, and Uncle John knew that the Englishman (nominally working under Japanese supervision) was organising all sorts of schemes for the relief of sickness and misery among P.O.W.'s and Internees. If he was found out no mercy would be shown him.

Therefore when Uncle John felt that the watch on himself might result in the discovery of Selwyn-Clarke's activities, he told Nellie about his fears. She said she would try to arrange an alternative meeting place. True to her word, the next time Uncle John came, she told him that on the following Sunday he should go across the harbour to the island. The meeting with Selwyn-Clarke would be at the house of Mrs. Sophie Odell in Pokfulam.

Uncle John's relief when he learned this was enormous. It meant that he would not have to sit in fear that at any moment a group of Kempeitai would burst in and find him and Nellie Lee plotting what would undoubtedly be treated as treasonable acts.

There was a strange uneasiness in him when he found Sophie Odell's house. These would be strangers to him, and there would doubtless be feelings of suspicion in the air. He went right up to the door, but when only a couple of steps from it, he stopped and wondered whether he shouldn't walk away again. He wasn't at all sure that he could go through with this. With Nellie it was one thing, but he knew Nellie well now, and never felt any awkwardness about talking to her. But these were strangers. And he was Japanese. He remembered what Nellie had told him about the Hong Kong people's hatred of everything Japanese. Well, the Odells were Hong Kong people. He was about to turn away and leave when he remembered why he was coming here. The reason was for the men's sake, the men who so desperately depended on his help.

Sophie Odell and her sister-in-law were charming. At first they were a little reticent in front of him, but the arrival of Selwyn-Clarke and the warm way in which he greeted Uncle John broke down the reticence. It was a happy occasion of much laughter and interesting conversation. Uncle John was particularly pleased that all those who were present understood his own feelings of loyalty towards Japan. He was not expected to agree with views as to who would win the war, nor did he have to sit through conversations in which Japan was maligned.

'No, war is war,' Sophie said, 'and naturally people are on one side or the other. But what baffles me is why there should be so much cruelty. Some of the things that have been done here by, if you'll pardon me, Uncle John, *your* people you just wouldn't believe.'

'Unfortunately, I know some of these things,' Uncle John said. 'But what can I say? I deplore what has happened. I can only think that maybe war brings with it a madness.'

'Madness, craziness, it must be something like that,' someone in the group said.

'Now look here, Uncle John hasn't come here to hear Japan maligned, ladies and gentlemen.' It was Selwyn-Clarke, and his soft voice commanded instant attention. 'After all he is taking great risks. We mustn't be so ungracious as to ...'

'But please,' Uncle John cut in, 'people have their feelings. Just one thing I would like to say, please; *please* do not judge all Japan and Japanese by the things you have experienced.' He was

66

embarrassed, unsure of how to conclude what he had started. 'War, you see, is so evil, it brings out evil. If you want to think of ordinary Japanese without madness, try to think of people like me, only better.'

There, it was out, and though he felt unworthy of some of the fine people he had known back in Japan, he hoped these people would understand what he was trying to tell them.

In the evening, going back from the Odells' place, Uncle John was still thinking over what he had been saying. The cruelty of his fellow countrymen was inexplicable to him. He could find no reason in it. Because he felt this way, he was certain that the things he had tried to get across to the people back there in Pokfulam must have sounded devoid of personal conviction. The whole business was paradoxical. The only thing he felt really certain of was that if his country had been Christian, this barbarity could not have happened—at least not to the same extent.

Not that he thought the enemy was entirely free of badness. He knew that badness was there on both sides. But there were limits—there was an agreement called the Geneva Convention ... men didn't *have* to inflict pain needlessly. This was what worried him, apart altogether from the offence to his instincts as a Christian. When the war ended, no matter who won (and he had no doubts but that Japan would emerge victorious), people with memories would tell of the things that had happened. Then his country would be displayed to the rest of the world as a place which nurtured and condoned cruelty. This knowledge upset him.

The Hong Kong Summer was now at its height. The humidity caused his shirt and trousers to cling to his body, and sweat ran in rivulets which itched and inched off his forehead and into his eyes.

The camp would be smelling atrociously when he got back. He was in no hurry.

Going down the hill ahead of him he saw the figures of two

67

Chinese Haka women. They were trotting along barefooted, bending under the weight of enormous loads of dry grass. This stuff they used for fuel as the Colony was almost bereft of timber. The women gathered the sunbaked grass and ferns off the sides of the hills, working for hours until they had as much as they could carry. Then they bundled it up, slung it across their shoulders, and padded miles back to their shack dwellings. One good blaze and the result of hours of back-breaking toil in hot sun would be rendered to ash. But it was the only way they could cook the life-giving rice and fish.

Poor people, Watanabe thought, you too are suffering badly. They had no means of earning a livelihood; there was very little food available to them; disease was widespread. Of course he knew that conditions had turned many of Hong Kong's people into desperate looters who had torn shops and private houses asunder as soon as the bombardment had started. He had seen the urchins coming daringly up to the wire at the camp and selling 'dysentery buns' to the prisoners at fantastic prices—and he had often closed his eyes with horror when the sentries fired at these children.

However, familiarity with these things in no way lessened his unpleasant reactions to them. There were stories of cannibalism, of hunger-crazed Chinese squatting in the Hong Kong gutters to eat the flesh of one of their numbers who had lain down to die in the street.

The two Haka women were still well ahead of him when a military truck roared round a corner which they were approaching. The two women jumped for their lives as the vehicle, deliberately it seemed, swerved towards them. They got up and were dusting themselves and examining the abrasions on their legs when the truck came to a halt, then reversed towards them.

Uncle John saw the two occupants, Japanese soldiers, getting out and going to the women. Then he heard the shouts as the soldiers struck out at the women.

'Filthy thieves! You have been stealing!'

The women were punched and kicked. Then one of the soldiers, the one with the bayonet-clad rifle, ripped the ties which kept the grass in bundles. He dumped most of the grass over the wall which stopped cars from careering down the slope into the sea. The grass was whipped away by the wind.

The women set up a wailing at this, but they were promptly silenced when the man with the bayonet turned on them and brandished the weapon. With one of his lunges he caught the tip of the blade in the hem of one woman's black shirt. When he continued the stroke upwards, the garment was ripped right up the front. It was the old woman that this happened to, and for a moment there was the glimpse of a shrivelled breast. There was a shout of laughter from the soldier as the woman, with an ageless shyness, tried to cover up her nakedness.

Uncle John drew level with the group.

'Why do you have to do this?' he asked the soldiers.

'Because they were stealing,' the laughing one answered.

'Stealing grass?' Uncle John said. 'Is it now a crime to "steal" dead grass?'

'They had no right to it,' the soldier answered. 'It belongs to the Imperial Japanese Army. And anyway, what business is it of yours old man? If you are not careful I will rip your nice clean suit so that you will be just like the old hag there.'

The second soldier joined in now.

He said: 'Who are you? One of our fine Japanese for whom Japan is not good enough I suppose. Living here in comfort no doubt when you should have been at home preparing for war. But we don't need your type. I have a good mind to run my bayonet through you.'

Uncle John was about to tell them that he too was in Hong Kong with the Japanese forces, but he knew it would be pointless. Worse, they might kill him on the spot for daring to intercede for the Chinese women.

The women were looking at him puzzled, not knowing what the tirade meant, not knowing whose side he was on. When the soldiers climbed back into their truck and drove away, he turned sympathetically towards the Haka women, but they were already busy trying to recover a few wisps of the scattering grass. And even if they had been looking at him, he wouldn't have been able to make himself understood. The Haka are hardly understood by the ordinary Chinese residents of Hong Kong—they are a lone people who speak their own dialect.

Uncle John was despondent.

*   *   *

Before he got inside the gates of the camp, the smell was already in his nose. It was a smell of disease, the stench of human bodies rotting away even though still alive.

At times he craved a numbness to sights around him. If only he could reach the saturation point at which he might cease to be sensitive to the sufferings and degradation. But no. If anything, he was becoming hypersensitive.

He just couldn't help smelling the filth of the dysentery, or seeing the shrunken men with the staring eyes and grotesque beards, or the bloated ones swollen to pitiful shapes by beri-beri. There were too many men with slits for eyes, with faces puffed up out of all recognition. And there was no escape from these things. Not even in sleep.

Uncle John was full of admiration for the camp doctors who never ceased trying, and who worked wonders with the scraps of material, men and medical, at their disposal. Whenever his thoughts turned to doctors, he knew he couldn't fail them. There could be no counting the cost.

The next time Nimori came to the camp he scarcely glanced at Watanabe. Uncle John bowed respectfully towards the officer but was ignored. Once, when he looked up, he caught Nimori looking at him. Uncle John pretended to be very busy.

The smuggling trips went on, and Selwyn-Clarke never ceased to be grateful. Sometimes it was drugs, sometimes antitoxin and vitamins, and very frequently money. Uncle John didn't know exactly how the money was used, but it certainly was highly prized by Ashton-Rose to whom he delivered it.

He got to know many of the prisoners by name, and whenever he could, he brought in various necessities to them, particularly salt. For people who, in a climate like Hong Kong's, might sweat away anything up to five pints of perspiration in a day, salt was a necessity to keep alive.

Whenever he could, he brought messages in and out for the H.K.V.D.C. people. One day, however, just as he was approaching a little knot of P.O.W.'s, he got a sudden feeling that he was being watched. He looked around him and saw that he was within sight of the camp office. As his gaze went in that direction, he saw a face drawing back from one of the windows, a face that had been looking straight at him.

Deliberately he let one of the sheafs of paper he was holding flutter to the ground. When he stooped to retrieve it he man aged another fleeting look towards the camp office. Yes, they were watching him all right. Another face, half obscured by the shine on the glass, was staring in his direction. The face disappeared when Uncle John straightened up and turned to the window.

In the office that afternoon, conversation was centred on the subject of 'animals who helped the enemy'. He knew it was for his benefit, even though his name was never once directly mentioned. Neither was he brought into the conversation by invitation or question of any sort.

They were talking, or rather discussing, what particular type of punishment should be dished out to any such 'animals' who were caught.

One man said he thought they should be publicly beheaded, as examples to others who might have inclinations to help the enemy.

'Oh no,' a voice opined, 'that way they would die too soon.

71

Such dogs should be made to suffer first before they die. Use them for bayonet practice perhaps?'

Someone else said: 'Or target practice. Our shooting must be very bad by now.'

After a little while the first voice said: 'It is believed that somebody in this camp is helping the British.'

'Yes, he thinks he is clever. But they all get caught, even the cleverest. He'll be caught too—caught in the act. And then...'

The sentence was left unfinished, waiting for its effect to sink home.

Then it carried on: 'If it's bayonet practice, I'm applying. I want to be in at the kill.'

Uncle John left his place and went outside to the lavatory, looking neither to the left nor right as he went out of the room. There was someone in the lavatory. He'd have to wait. But it was better than going back inside. Or was it—were they carrying on like this just to drive him out and to see him getting scared?

He went straight back in and sat down. The talk carried on as before, but he managed to block out the sense of it by talking mentally to God; this way he actually got a certain amount of comfort. Just before he finished praying, he slipped in a special plea for Nellie's three children.

*   *   *

The year thinned away to its close. Those in the camp continued to get sick. Some died; others clung to life. Some got lousy, and, their morale completely dissipated, they didn't care.

Uncle John heard about it one day when a British officer came to him and asked if it would be permissible to put one room aside to use as a delousing centre. The Britisher, obviously

72

hating what he was forced to say, described how the worst of those who were infested often had lumps of living matter hanging in such places as under the armpits. Other men, he said, got sick at the sight of the flesh sagging from the weight of the heaving lice. The terrible thing, he said, was that the unfortunate ones who were afflicted, had had all their instinctive feelings of cleanliness blunted away to nothingness.

The room was set aside and the poor wretches who were placed in there were unmercifully scrubbed clean.

The letters that came and went from and to Takasho Street never made mention of these things. Mitsuko's letters were full of warmth and longing. Occasionally she passed on odd snippets of information about the two boys, but that was the only way she ever touched on war. She told how the babies—though they were now babies no longer—were growing up into fine young women.

Uncle John tried to picture Kimi and Kei. When he ran out of descriptions of Hong Kong, he turned instead to asking more and more questions about the children. He wanted to know everything about them, their studies, who they resembled, if they were obedient. Occasionally childish letters from them were enclosed with Mitsuko's, and these Uncle John kept in his breast pocket close to his heart.

He told Mitsuko repeatedly that he was looking forward to the day when they would be reunited to be a family once more. He began to live for this time. He sometimes lay in bed drawing up lists of the things he would do when he got back to Hiroshima, and the things he would do when he retired, and where he would take Mitsuko and the family to live. Then he'd fall asleep, happy with thoughts of old times and of the times to come.

The following mornings always brought their awakenings. There were hundreds of men lamed with 'Hong Kong Foot'—a disease which rotted the feet away and sometimes drove sufferers crazy with the pain—and there were men whose bodies were covered in weeping ulcers.

Shamshui Po camp was a human cess pit. The details of the place were more horrifying than any nightmare. Its stench was like nothing else he had ever experienced. But for the periodic visits he paid to Nellie's flat, and to the Odell's place at Pokfulam, Uncle John would have gone insane.

*   *   *

'At the time of the attack on Hong Kong, I was manager of the Mercantile Bank there and, after the surrender, was interned in a Chinese doss house on the waterfront. This place was called the Sun Wah, and I was sent there in company with the other British and American Bankers when the majority of civilian internees were sent to Stanley.

'Although we were supposed to be confined, except when taken out under guard, the control was a bit loose, and Sophie Odell and her sister-in-law (they were not interned) got in to see some of us. One or two of us broke out occasionally on Sundays and went to their house at Pokfulam. It was there that I first met John Watanabe, and I found him, with his quiet manner, so wishing to be helpful—even if the possibilities of being able to do much were almost negligible.

'After meeting him a few times at Pokfulam, one could not but take a great liking to him as a sincere good man, totally different to the other Japanese surrounding us. We were aware that he was trying to help in improving conditions in the Shamshui Po Camp, and helping to get diphtheria medicines in for the diphtheria outbreak.

'Things tightened up after the middle of 1942. Further visits to Pokfulam became impossible, as were visits by outsiders to us. John Watanabe however came to visit us in the Sun Wah, and I will always remember his visit on Christmas Day, 1942. He joined four of us in singing carols, gave us a solo rendering of

74

"Holy Night" in Japanese, *and contributed to enhancing our*
meagre diet.'

H.W. Hawkins
(Formerly Manager,
Mercantile Bank, Hong Kong)

CHAPTER VII

Christmas 1942 was like no other Christmas Kiyoshi Watanabe remembered. It was a time of deep loneliness for him. Previously this time of year had been essentially a period of happiness. He loved the nostalgia of it, the mystery, the excitement of the children, the present-giving, the hush of midnight when Christmas Eve became Christmas Day. Most of all he loved the memories Christmas evoked.

Christmas, he used to tell Mitsuko, is the childrens' time; but part of the delight it brought to himself was made up of varied recollections of his childhood. Not that the feast of Christmas had ever been observed in his own family, but when he saw the expressions of happiness and surprise on the faces of Miwa and Kimi and Kei and the others, it stirred memories from the time when he too had been young and full of the capacity to be pleasantly surprised.

Christmas 1942 was very different.

For a start, the surroundings were all wrong. The family was dispersed, many hundreds of miles separating them. December 25th and what it stood for had to be a purely personal thing for him. Words like '...and Peace on Earth to men of Good Will...' had a hollow ring about them. They seemed, in a sense, to be an expression of some awful cynicism.

On the week preceding Christmas he took to walking alone in the darkness of the prison camp trying to conjure up mental pictures of other Christmases he had known. Sometimes he came very close to success, but then, the moan of a sick man or the barking of the guard dogs would crash in and destroy the picture. He'd try to bring the picture back. Inevitably he failed.

Confused images fought for lucidity in his mind. He would think of Bethlehem and '... there was no more room for them at the inn', and then he would think of 5,000 men crammed together behind barbed wire entanglements. He would think of the dilemma of Mary and Joseph looking for a spot in which their baby could be born; and then he would think of the thousands of mothers and fathers in England and Canada and Australia waiting for news from their sons in the prison camps. Many of them would never hear. He thought of the joy the birth of a little refugee boy had brought; and then he thought of the agony the deaths of so many prisoners would bring.

And then he would go to his bed and cry because he couldn't pray and because he couldn't understand a lot of the Why's that whirled through his mind.

Presently, when he calmed down, he would begin to pray, or at least to try.

*   *   *

Colonel Tokunaga didn't know whether to ignore Watanabe or have him executed. There had been many complaints from the Shamshui Po prison staff. As far as he personally was concerned, there wasn't anything about the man he could find fault with. Watanabe was always neat, always respectful. He seemed a meek little man.

But Tokunaga knew the others distrusted the ex-pastor. That was another thing he didn't understand. Not being a Christian himself, he was at a loss to know why anyone should want to take up this Christianity business. Nimori was always saying it was a sign of weakness and a sign that a man didn't think enough of Japan and its traditional religions. But then Nimori was fanatical.

Of course Watanabe certainly seemed too soft-hearted. And yet, though he was easily frightened, there didn't appear to be much fear in the man. Not enough to put him off anything he took it into his mind to do and keep on doing. Tokunaga was puzzled.

Outside in the passageway Interpreter Watanabe waited to be summoned into the presence of the colonel. He had been waiting an hour now, and from the small amount of traffic in and out of the colonel's office, he felt sure the colonel wasn't all that busy. He didn't even hear the senior officer talking on the phone.

Watanabe was full of apprehension. He didn't know exactly why he had been summoned to Prince Edward Road, but felt sure it wasn't for any pleasant reason. So he sat in a state of nervous tension until eventually an orderly came out and said the colonel was ready to see him now.

Tokunaga did not acknowledge his salute when he went in. The colonel was holding some papers, but Watanabe thought he was probably not looking at them. At times like this he could feel sorry for Tokunaga, because the man was in a quandary and was so clearly searching his mind for an answer. But the gravity of his own situation did not escape him either.

At this moment too he felt very much *Interpreter* Watanabe. *Uncle John* was a different character, somebody with whom he could not identify himself.

He waited for the colonel to speak.

'Of course you know why I have sent for you, Watanabe,' the other man began.

'No sir,' Watanabe said, and his voice sounded small, and he cleared his throat to take the fear out of his voice.

'Don't interrupt!' the colonel said, and already his anger was rising. 'I've sent for you because I have had repeated complaints from Shamshui Po about you. I'm undecided as to what to do. The men you work with say they don't trust you, that you are not one hundred per cent Japanese in your outlook, and that you are dangerous. You must have given them some cause to make complaints like this. Luckily for you they have no proof of anything you have done, otherwise I would have no hesitation about my duty.'

The colonel got up. He picked up his samurai sword and inspected the intricate tracery on it. He was searching around in his mind for what he would next say.

The colonel put the sword down again.

'Why do you have to be like this, Watanabe? Why do I have to have trouble with you? Don't you think I have enough to think about in this stinking place without having to cope with a damned civilian Japanese interpreter?'

He wasn't really expecting answers. He was merely voicing the thoughts that annoyed him most. Uncle John kept his silence.

'I don't know what you have been doing to make the others complain. I've got a good idea of what you have *not* been doing. But you have aroused the suspicions and dislike of the men you work with, and my first reaction is to send you back to Japan in disgrace.'

The colonel was in full swing now, and Uncle John knew that the solution would probably come out in the next burst of speech.

'You see, your trouble is that you forget you have to be firm, and where necessary harsh, with these prisoners of war. They are our enemies, remember that. They may be prisoners, but they are still our enemies. And from everything I have heard, you are far too kind to these enemies. I'll give you another chance. I'm going to take you out of Shamshui Po Camp and send you to the hospital at Bowen Road. There Major Saito will keep his eye on you. I'll get a replacement for you at Shamshui Po and send you to Bowen Road. And I don't want any more complaints. Now get out.'

Interpreter Watanabe paid the customary respects and left the colonel's office.

Well, he was leaving Shamshui Po at last. That meant that Inouye and Matsudo and Sekiguchi and all the others would be left behind, and he would be in cleaner surroundings. At the same time his feelings were tinged with regret too because there were many faces he had begun to look upon as friendly.

On the other hand, he was going to a place from which attempted escapes were unlikely. He would be away from the ordeal of camp shootings. As he made his way back to the camp, he thought about the nights he had lain awake wondering who was planning to get through the wire and make for the Castlepeak road. And the mornings he had looked across Laichikok Bay wondering what secrets it could tell, sad secrets of men who thought about and tried to swim across it. He thought of the reprisals, the sufferings of the ones left behind. The document the prisoners were made to sign stating they would not attempt to escape. The looks on their faces as they signed. The whispered words: 'under duress, there's no bloody need to keep to this mate.'

All this was behind now.

He smiled wryly as he packed his clothes ready for the move to Bowen Road. There was the leather brief-case from Selwyn-Clarke, the *feruski* in which he had taken the food to Nellie Lee and her children. And the bed under which the precious anti-toxin and instruments had been hidden.

He left the camp with the minimum of fuss. In view of Tokunaga's warnings, he daren't say goodbye to any of the men he had befriended. As he walked out of the gates, his thoughts turned back to the many times he had made the inward journey quaking with fright lest he should be caught.

This too was over. The hospital would hardly need anyone to smuggle in drugs. Relief was the biggest part of his reactions as he left Shamshui Po.

*   *   *

Bowen Road Military Hospital is built high up on the side of a hill. The view from there, even in wartime, was magnificent.

In 1944, when its new interpreter reported there, the hospital was staffed by British military personnel who had, as their chief, Major Saito, a doctor in the Imperial Japanese army. Doctor Saito was far more of an army officer than a doctor. Uncle John's first impressions of the man were of a person who had lost all his love for surgery and had become enamoured of the power vested in the officers of any service.

Uncle John had hardly arrived there before he was in trouble with Saito. In the office, two days after first reporting for duty, the telephone rang with an outside call. Just as he picked up the phone, Saito walked into the office.

Uncle John answered the phone in Japanese. A woman's voice at the other end said: 'Hello! Hello! May I talk to Mr. Watanabe please? Hello! Hello! Do you hear me? May I talk to Mr. Watanabe, M-i-s-t-e-r W-a-t-a-n-a-b-e, *please....*'

Uncle John recognised the voice of Nellie Lee.

Major Saito said: 'Well, who is it, Watanabe?'

'Please sir, it is for me.'

Saito's jaw sagged in surprise, then he drew his lips together in an expression of anger.

'Hello! Hello! Nellie,' Uncle John said, 'Nellie, I am sorry, it is not convenient for me to talk with you now.'

'Oh it's *you*, Uncle John? Gee, I wondered where you'd got to! O.K. fine, as long as I know where you are. Are you all right?'

'Yes, yes Nellie. I am all right. Goodbye.'

Saito was standing over him.

'So it's Nellie! And who is Nellie? I suppose you've got your women just like Nimori and the rest of them.'

'No, no sir, she is not my woman, she is just a friend.'

This sounded thin even to Uncle John, but he had never thought about it before. How could anyone think...

'Well, whatever she is, you ought to know you can't have women, or anyone else for that matter, ringing you up here.

What do you think this place is, a hotel? By right you people shouldn't associate with anyone from Hong Kong. You should stick to your own kind, to your own people. I forbid you to have anyone else telephoning you at this hospital.'

This was hardly a good start for Uncle John, and he kept out of Saito's way as much as possible after that.

The cleanliness of the hospital was startling after the squalor of the camp. Even though people were in there because of wounds or disease, there was a completely different atmosphere in the scrubbed wards through which the British doctors and medical orderlies moved quietly and efficiently. It was silent up here on the Peak. The city sprawled out down below, and the miniscule life in the far-down streets seemed detached, almost like a working model when viewed from high above.

This was a place in which it was far easier to feel at peace, and Uncle John sometimes went into the hospital grounds at evening time and looked out to sea towards where the islands lay softly rounded by the haze. Occasionally his eyes strayed across the bay towards Kowloon, then past the Typhoon anchorage until he was looking at Shamshui Po. From this distance it was hard to imagine the misery down there.

Each morning a roll call established that none of the amputees or TB cases or cancer patients had escaped during the night. The uselessness of this bit of red tape at first made Uncle John edgy. Then he accepted it as part and parcel of the military's way of working.

As the sole interpreter in the hospital, he soon found that many of the tensions which had made life almost unbearable for him in Shamshui Po, were non-existent in Bowen Road. He still had much the same kind of duties to perform, but there were no prying eyes apart from those of Saito.

Major Saito was another who seemed to have developed the capacity to let the hurts and pains of others slip by him unnoticed. The man was hard and utterly devoid of sentimentality and feeling. However, as long as he kept out of his way, Uncle John knew he had no others to fear at the hospital.

Very soon he was able to put faces to all the names on the list of patients which hung in his office. These were men he had not met before. By his attitude and general demeanour, he hoped to penetrate the barrier of distrust which the patients had thrown up around themselves on the arrival of this stranger in their midst.

He would often stop by a bed and ask its occupant how he was feeling. The first time he did this, the man turned his face away into the pillow and didn't even reply. Uncle John felt all the others in the ward looking at him. When he raised his head and tried to catch their eyes, they too turned from him and ignored him.

He left the ward. These men were going to be hard to get through to, and this reaction to his friendliness distressed him. He would have to try again, and keep on trying until they realised he was not endeavouring to trick them.

The next day he stopped at the same bed. Again the man turned away, though this time with not quite the same finality.

Uncle John repeated his enquiry every day for a week until in the end he got a grudging 'I'm all right ... no thanks to you.'

'I am glad,' Uncle John said, 'I shall say a prayer for you.'

'You'll *what*? Say a prayer for me! Blimey that's a good one! Who do Nips pray to?'

'To the same One you pray to.'

Uncle John tried to shut from his mind the man's use of the insulting word.

The man looked incredulous.

'You mean to tell me you're a ... that you ...'

'That I'm a Christian—yes.'

'Well I'll be—hey! Hear that fellas. The interpreter here's a flippin' Christian, like us. Least he says he is.'

After that it wasn't so hard. Gradually the patients grew to trust him. With so many less people here than at Shamshui Po, he was able to take an interest in them all, and he learned many things about them.

83

Some of the Canadian boys became desperately lonely, particularly those suffering from post-operative depression. These he tried to comfort by making conversation. A few of the younger ones thawed out and took wrinkled snapshots from their pockets and passed them shyly to him. He saw smiling girls posing self-consciously in the Canadian snow, and grubby children pouting because they had been made to stand still outside timbered houses. He talked to these men about their wives and girl friends, and he told them about his own wife and children.

When he brought an autograph book and asked them if they would write in it for him, they eagerly said yes, these Canadians with the names and addresses he couldn't even pronounce—like A. D. Rheault who came from Reddit, Ontario, and Valmont Le Bouef, Hill Side Street, Campellton, New Brunswick.

For the Canadians he felt particularly sorry. The men of the Winnipeg Grenadiers were not long enough in Hong Kong to make many friends when they were pitched into battle. Therefore, subsequently, when other prisoners, men of the Middlesex Regiment, the RASC, RAOC, Scots Guards, RAF, Navy and others, had parcels sent into them, the Canadians in most cases just lay and waited, knowing that the waiting was futile because no one in the Colony knew of their existence as individuals.

It grieved Uncle John to see feelings of being alone and unwanted registering on the faces of the Canadian boys. He decided to try to right the situation.

Some time previously, looking for a book shop, he had come across a small well-stocked establishment in Ice House Street. The owner was a Russian Jew named Pasco who, when the Japanese came into Hong Kong, had lost his premises in the Gloucester Hotel. He had found the only other site available was the one at Ice House Street.

During many visits to the shop, Uncle John struck up a friendship with Mr. Pasco. Pasco's original wariness wore down before the interpreter's naïvety. He came to accept Uncle John as a friend.

Therefore it was to Ice House Street, to the shop of Mr. Pasco, that Uncle John now went. In his pocket he had a list of names.

In the shop he had to bide his time while a young Japanese officer browsed through some art books. Then he approached Mr. Pasco and put his problem to him.

Mr. Pasco listened patiently. Yes, he had heard that parcels were sent to Shamshui Po, and that Hilda Selwyn-Clarke was doing great work in providing comforts for Bowen Road. He would be pleased to help Uncle John in any way he could, but How?

Uncle John took the small list from his pocket.

'These are some of the boys who never get anything,' he told Pasco. 'Most of them are Canadians. Now, provided parcels are delivered at the hospital properly addressed to someone on the inside, they will be officially accepted and handed over to the people whose names appear on them. This is where I hope you will help me. Can you get some of your friends to make up some parcels and send them to these men on this list?'

Pasco was hesitant at first. Could this not be a trick, subtly led up to, to land him and his family and friends into the hands of the Kempeitai? Perhaps this Watanabe was a cunning agent of the secret police.

But when he looked at the man, Pasco knew that his suspicion was no more than a fear-inspired notion. That's what war did to you—made you suspicious of *everyone*. Watanabe's honesty of purpose was so obvious that there could be no doubting it.

'But aren't you taking a dreadful risk bringing lists like that out of the hospital?' Pasco asked.

'A risk? Yes, I suppose it is a risk,' Uncle John said, 'but you must believe me Mr. Pasco, I do not care if it is only my life that is at stake.'

Pasco stared at this Japanese who stood there on the other side of the book counter and made such a strange statement. He had never before heard a man say something so reeking of mock heroism. And yet the manner of its saying was devoid of any brashness, or the other thing that might have been there instead, the holier-than-thou chest-thumping piety. This interpreter fellow was self-effacing and sincere.

'Look, I don't pretend to understand you, Mr. Watanabe,' Pasco said, 'but if it's what you really want, I'll do my best to arrange some parcels for this weekend.'

'And the addresses, Mr. Pasco, you won't forget to put them on?'

'No, I won't forget.'

'You are very kind, Mr. Pasco. God will reward you.'

A week later a new lot of parcels arrived at the hospital. Uncle John himself checked them in. There was one for every name that had been on the list he had handed over to the man from the book shop in Ice House Street.

That day the Canadians' faces were no longer drawn serious by loneliness and disappointment when the parcels were being distributed. They were shining-eyed with surprise as parcels were handed to each of them.

There were buzzes of conversation, half-caught phrases like 'There must be some mistake...' '...I can't understand it—a parcel for *me*?' 'Me too? But from where? Who'd send *me* a parcel?'

Uncle John looked around at their faces. Then he turned and went towards the door. Just then someone said: 'I bet Mr. Watanabe knows something about this. Do you, Mr. Watanabe?'

A soldier from Manitoba was standing up by his bed. Silence came down like a whiplash on the room. Uncle John waved his hand in embarrassment.

'What are you saying?' he said. 'I do not understand.'

'I guess you understand all right,' the soldier said. 'And I'd like to say thanks on behalf of the other guys and myself. I ... eh ... I'm no good at puttin' things, y'know, nicely and all that, and I ... eh ... ah   anyway Mr. Watanabe, what I mean is—thanks a lot.'

Uncle John shook his head in a sort of denial.

'I don't know what you are saying,' he said.

He walked out of the room. Behind him a chorus of voices rose up from the beds. 'Thanks ... thanks a lot, Mr. Watanabe ... yeah, thanks a lot....'

This is stupid, he thought. They shouldn't thank me. They should thank Mr. Pasco and his friends. They should not thank me like this. This is stupid.

*   *   *

When Dr. Selwyn-Clarke was finally arrested, Uncle John was shattered. Somehow or other, the idea of the doctor being arrested had, for a long time, been something Uncle John refused to even contemplate.

Of course the Britisher had been taking many risks, but nothing he did could really be construed as the work of a saboteur. He was a doctor. As such he was totally concerned with the preservation of human life. It mattered not to him whether the people he felt needed his help were prisoners or not. The main thing, whether their skins were white, dark or yellow, was that they were human beings. Therefore no man-made regulations would stand in his way.

Uncle John knew that Selwyn-Clarke never allowed them to either. The doctor had a whole chain of people, Chinese, Portuguese, anyone and everyone he could trust, working for him. The interpreter felt privileged that he too had been one of the links. It was an underground system whose sole object was, not to destroy, but to preserve.

When Uncle John learned that 'this great and good man' was now a prisoner, he was shattered. He was at a complete loss to

87

know what he should do. The doctor, he reasoned, would in all probability have had to deny everything in order to save those who had been of assistance to him. If he, Uncle John, were to enter the picture in any way now, he would accomplish little other than to further incriminate Selwyn-Clarke and his helpers, and perhaps be responsible for a worsening of the doctor's torture.

The sleepless nights started again. Up here in the quietness of Bowen Road there was nothing to disturb the long hours. Nothing but his thoughts of what might be happening in the cells down there in the city to the quiet-voiced doctor. The helplessness and the hopelessness of his predicament bore heavily on him. Nellie Lee was the only one with whom he could share it.

He went to her, and they sat and talked for hours on end. These were conversations full of conjecture and self-incrimination. Whenever Nellie tried to break in, he would harshly stop her. He had to talk, to try to get it out of his system, to try for a solution. In the end he succeeded in talking a lot of the confusion out of his mind. Then he felt better. From now on he would try not to allow worry use up too much of his nervous energy. He would need all of that to keep on finding ways to help the men at Bowen Road.

'You must be careful, Uncle John,' Nellie said as he was leaving. 'I know I'm always telling you that, but I have heard rumours that the Kempeitai are only waiting for you to make one slip. They've got Doctor Selwyn-Clarke. It's your turn next.'

'As long as you and your children keep on praying for me, Nellie, I shall be all right.'

'Oh, we'll keep on doing that. But how are you able to keep on believing? That's what beats me. When I think of all that has happened, and is still happening, I don't know how you can still believe so strongly.'

'Whatever happens is the will of God, Nellie,' he told her.

How often, recently, he had found himself on the knife-edge

of doubt about that. But now, as he said it to Nellie, his faith was as strong as ever.

*   *   *

Major Carter was dying.

He may have known this. If he did, he never revealed it. Outwardly, he was all good humour and zest for living, though of course he was unable to leave his bed.

Major Carter was one of the first people in the hospital Uncle John had got to know by name. Mainly because the major was just about the most conspicuous person you saw when you entered his ward.

He sat in bed propped up by a high pile of pillows which helped him to remain in an upright position. The first time Uncle John saw him, he pitied him. The rubber and glass tubes which stuck out of the major seemed to call for some kind of pity. But when he got to know the man, Uncle John discovered that Carter's personality and attitude were not geared to the reception of sympathy.

Sometimes, when Uncle John's spirits sank, he would think of Carter sitting there laughing and making those around him laugh too. Uncle John remembered that once, in 1942, when censoring letters, he had come across one written by Carter to his wife.

Though never able to get over the conviction that reading other men's private mail was an intrusion into something sacred, he nevertheless had to submerge his personal feelings in order to carry out his official duty. When he was able to read these letters in as detached a way as possible, he was often struck by the manner in which these men expressed themselves. He took to jotting down little extracts from these letters—phrases which were new to him, or which said beautiful things.

And phrases which illustrated the things he himself believed about the human character.

On that day in 1942 when Carter's letter was the next one in the batch he had been working on, Uncle John had scribbled down three sentences from it. These were simply: 'My love darling, as always, for you. Did you receive my last cable, and did you take refuge in the advice: "No news is good news?"'

That was all. Uncle John wondered what the exact reason was that he had copied down those words. Probably, he thought, because they expressed something of the hope which is said to spring eternal in the human breast. When he looked at the words, he wondered a lot about the woman to whom they were penned. How much did she know?

Uncle John asked one of the hospital's British doctors in confidence what Major Carter's illness was.

'I'm afraid it's something we are powerless to cure,' the doctor said. 'It's cancer. Cancer of the oesophagus. That's the gullet, just here, near the throat.'

'And he will not live?' Uncle John asked.

The doctor shook his head.

'Do you know when he will die?' Uncle John asked.

'I don't know. Could be six weeks, or six months. It's hard to say. He's got a tremendous will to live, poor chap. But it's only a matter of time really.'

'I wish I could do something,' Uncle John said. It seemed such an inadequate thing to say.

'The best thing you can do is not to let on to him anything that I've told you,' the doctor said.

Uncle John said: 'He is a brave man.'

'One of the bravest,' the doctor answered.

Uncle John felt for the doctor. With all the training he had done, all the medical theory he knew, there was nothing in the world he could do for Carter. He could only stand by and watch his patient slipping slowly but surely out of his grasp. The knowledge must be bitter, Uncle John thought.

The weeks lengthened into months. Carter's face grew thinner and more gaunt. But whatever pain he suffered, he never complained. Those around him were kept in a state of almost perpetual good humour by this man who chose to poke fun at his appearance and at the feeding contraption sticking out of his belly.

Uncle John's nightly prayer sessions were growing longer and longer. There were so many people, so many things, he had to pray for. But, no matter how tired he was nor how long he was on his knees, he never got into bed without praying for Carter. The man was proving an inspiration to him.

Carter laughed when Uncle John asked him if he would write something in the autograph book.

'Sure,' Carter said, 'I'd be pleased to, but what can I put? It's the old, old problem. You wouldn't want me to say "You asked me to write in your autograph book, put something original in..." No, no, that's as old as the hills. Too trite anyway. But then, I'm not profound or anything like that. Anyway, leave it with me, and I'll see if I can think of something.'

Uncle John handed him the book. It was a beige-coloured leather-covered one he had bought in a Hong Kong shop—probably at Pasco's. Inside the cover was the maker's name: John Walker & Co. Limited, Warwick Lane, London, E.C.4.

Sometimes Uncle John used to look at this small print to try to relate it to fact. The book was one of the 'Tuscan Series' No. 840. That meant nothing to him, so he dismissed it from his mind. But London, E.C.4—that gave him hours of thought. He didn't know what the letters stood for except that they obviously meant some area of London. He would try to visualise Warwick Lane, using as his only terms of reference the descriptions in the few Dickens' novels he had read. Otherwise he knew nothing of London apart from what he could pick out of the two English postcards in his possession. One showed Big Ben and the intricate-faced buildings below it which house the parliament of England. The other postcard showed the massive mound the world knows as St. Paul's cathedral.

He supposed he would never see London. Even if he lived through this war (and he often doubted it) he would be too old to travel. And where would he get the money?

'Is there any one particular page?' Carter was asking.

'Please, anywhere you wish,' Uncle John said.

Carter said: 'Right, just lend me a pencil and pen. I'll need both, because I'm no artist you know, and I want to be able to rub out if I have to.'

When Uncle John walked away from the bed space, Carter was cracking jokes with those closest to him.

'Picasso'll have nothing on me after this,' he was saying. 'You fellows are privileged to be in on the birth of a great new name in the world of art'

Uncle John, when he reached the door, looked back momentarily. The last impression he had before he went out was of Carter sitting there, his tubes waggling from side to side as he tried to settle himself into a more comfortable position. Uncle John wondered what he would draw in the book.

In the afternoon the doctor he had spoken to about Carter came to see the interpreter.

'Mr. Watanabe,' the doctor said, 'I know, as do many of us, that you've been a great help to a lot of the people here, and I wondered if I might ask a favour of you?'

Uncle John said: 'I shall do my best, doctor. What is it you want?'

'Thank you,' the doctor replied. 'It's not for me really, but you know you were interested in Major Carter's case?'

'Yes.'

'Well, we're in a spot of bother over that feeding apparatus. Some of the tubes need to be changed, and we haven't got any replacements here in the medical stores. I daren't ask Major Saito any more. I've kept on asking him, and now he won't even listen to me. Do you think, when you next go out, you might possibly try to get a set of tubes?'

'Yes,' Uncle John said. 'Of course, but please write down for me exactly what you require.'

The Britisher wrote out the specifications.

When he was finished, he said: 'I can't thank you enough for this.'

Uncle John waved away the other man's thanks. He hadn't even got the things yet. But he liked the doctor. He reminded him of Hidezi, kind and gentle, just as a doctor should be.

Uncle John folded the piece of paper with the doctor's writing on it and tucked it away deep in his pocket.

Carter still hadn't finished with the autograph book when Uncle John asked him for it. Indeed the major's mock embarrassment was peculiarly childish, and he made much play of tucking the book under his sheet, like an errant boy who hides something which shouldn't be in his possession at all.

The other men in the ward pulled Carter's leg about the whole affair and laughed. The sight of the men laughing made Uncle John smile. It was a good sight. He began to laugh himself with them, and then the padre walked in. A respectful silence descended on the room.

Uncle John, out of deference, decided to leave. Every evening at this time Padre Squire came in and said an evening prayer with the men. Uncle John felt he would only be an intruder if he stayed there unasked. The men, he felt, would feel inhibited if a Japanese were present, particularly if the padre wanted to say something of an even slightly propagandist nature in order to raise their morale. Besides, he didn't yet know Padre Squire all that well. So, he discreetly left the room and walked out into the gardens.

It was that hour of peace when the night's curtain begins to slip down over the sky and gently pushes the last of the daylight to its resting place. Uncle John moved slowly along the path.

Why couldn't all men take time out from war at this hour each day? he wondered. Stop shooting, and bombing and bayonetting each other, and just stand still and let the peace seep into their bones. Would they then ever be able to recommence their warring?

He stopped walking.

93

Through the trees he could see the lights coming on in Kowloon across the water. Swiftly, and yet imperceptibly, the night was drawing down.

Suddenly he became aware of a voice speaking somewhere behind and above him. He turned around and looked up. For the first time he realised that he had stopped under the open window of one of the wards. The voice was a familiar one, and then he identified it as that of Padre Squire. Uncle John listened. The words floated down, crystal clear in the moonlight.

'. . . say our prayer. "Lord of our Life, help us in the days when the burdens we carry chafe our shoulders and weigh us down; when the skies are grey and cheerless, and our souls have lost their courage. Then tune our hearts to brave music; turn our eyes to where the skies are full of promise, and unite us in comradeship with the Heroes and Saints of every age. For Christ's sake." '

The Japanese in the garden beneath the ward window joined his voice with the voices in the room above to say 'Amen'.

* * *

Finding the exact type of tubes for Major Carter's feeding apparatus was no easy matter. It took many hours of walking through the Kowloon and Victoria streets, many enquiries of friends from all walks of life. For a while Uncle John despaired of ever getting what he was looking for, but he wasn't going to give up that easily.

His persistence was rewarded at last. He slipped the rubber tubing into his briefcase. For a moment he was afraid the glass portions would be too long to fit, but careful manipulation eventually allowed them to slide in though with not a centimetre to spare.

He walked slowly and carefully lest anyone bump into him

and unwittingly smash the contents of the case. Time after time he stepped off footpaths rather than take the risk of being jostled. He mentally thanked Selwyn-Clarke for providing such a useful receptacle as the brief-case was proving to be; it would make things easier for getting the precious tubes into the hospital too.

This he managed with not too much trouble. The following morning he called the doctor who had asked him to get the tubes.

'Any luck?' the doctor asked.

Uncle John unwrapped the tubes and handed them over. The doctor was profuse in his thanks.

Later on, when Uncle John walked into Carter's ward for the roll-call, the major was grinning all across his face.

'The Doc tells me I've got you to thank for my new hubble-bubble outfit,' the major said, fingering the tubes. 'Thank you very much indeed. All I can do is to bequeath you this—my first and last masterpiece.'

He handed over the autograph book, a page held open so that Uncle John could look at it.

The major had done a simple line drawing of himself sitting in his bed with his pillows high behind him. In the cartoon, he was holding the feeding tubes with one hand. Underneath, printed neatly, it said: FOURTEEN MONTHS AND PUTTING ON WEIGHT! IS THIS A RECORD! (WITH APOLOGIES TO RIPLEY.)

It was signed: 'R. Carter, Major, F.A.'s Staff, H.Q. Hong Kong.'

So, he was still joking about himself and his appearance and his 'contraption'! There was certainly no thought in him of dying.

*   *   *

On September 14th, 1944, Major Carter died.

Uncle John went to his funeral in the hospital grounds. He could speak no word to anyone about the major's death. He didn't trust himself to talk. He was too full of grief.

Afterwards, he went back to his room. He took out the autograph book and opened the page on which the major had made the drawing. On the bottom left hand corner, under Carter's caption, he wrote a simple inscription in pencil:

'Died of cancer in the oesophagus (14 Sept. 1944) at the Bowen Road M. Hospital.'

CHAPTER VIII

Mitsuko Watanabe was worried. She sat at the table of her Takasho Street flat in Hiroshima and tried to concentrate. These days concentrating was difficult for her. She had so much on her mind, what with the problems of all her little kindergarten students, Kei living in a dormitory over in Kure—and on war work already although barely into her 'teens—Kimi commuting every day, and Miwa living fifteen hours' train journey away in Kiyushu. And the two boys away in the army.

But most of all she was worried about Kiyoshi, her husband. Ever since he had left for Hong Kong, Mitsuko had been worried. She knew he wasn't used to being buffeted, and she was perpetually concerned in case army life would be too tough for him.

His letters, in the beginning, came frequently and were full of a buoyancy which she suspected was largely contrived. As the months passed, the letters grew less in number and in bulk until eventually those that arrived seemed lacking in any details about himself. Sometimes Mitsuko's anxiety made her ask him, in her letters to him, direct questions which never got answers. All he would reply was that there was no need for her to worry; all he wanted of her were her prayers.

God knew she prayed for him often enough.

She was writing to him again now, and she gave him all the information he had asked for about the family. She also wrote at

97

length this time about things which could no longer be left unsaid. She told him of her serious worries about the war and the way things were going in the Pacific. Although she knew it was something no good Japanese should even countenance, she said, she had a feeling the Americans were going to start advancing right to the very doors of Japan upon which they would beat in anger.

If that ever happened, Hiroshima must surely become a target for bombers. Miwa, working as a midwife with Hidezi down in Kiyushu, had already hinted that it would be safer for the family to evacuate from the city. What did Kiyoshi think? Would he please write back soon and advise her what to do, and in future would he take care to write something about *himself* in his letters.

Mitsuko closed and sealed the envelope. She still had to write to Miwa. Then to the boys. But at the back of her mind all the time was the picture of the gentle man who was her husband.

Later that night, as she did every night, she went on her knees beside her bed. This was what *he* wanted.

*　　*　　*

Uncle John read Mitsuko's letter several times. It was different from any other he had received from her, and it caused him to think back on what he had been writing to her.

True, they had been sparse little notes recently, made up almost entirely of questions. He would have to do something about it, and now; but it was a problem to know what he could tell her about himself. It couldn't be anything which might arouse the suspicions of the censors. Indeed he wondered what Mitsuko had written which had been excised from this, her most recent letter. It must have been something relevant to the bit about Miwa's suggesting the family should evacuate. He hoped

98

Mitsuko wasn't going to get herself into trouble because of what the censor took out.

Well, anyway, he himself still had to find something to tell her. Preferably something that wouldn't upset her.

Finally he decided to tell her about his stomach trouble. He decided on this because the end of the story was that he had got better.

He wrote therefore of how, some months previously, he had been stricken with agonising stomach pains, so severe that they left him with the conviction that he must be suffering from something extremely serious. This, he said, was most likely the reason his letters had become so shallow and non-committal. He had been unable to give his whole mind to their writing.

However, to continue, the doctor had given him a most painstaking examination and could find nothing more serious wrong with him than teeth which were sadly in need of attention. The dentist, in his turn, was aghast at the sights that met his eyes once the Watanabe mouth was opened to him. He prescribed relatively simple treatment—wholesale extractions!

Uncle John described how, on one single afternoon, he became virtually toothless under local anaesthetic, and then, within hours, was sporting gleaming white dentures. Now, he said, he had a fine set of teeth, better looking than those with which Nature had endowed him in the beginning—and his health was back to normal.

He didn't mention that the doctor who had been so meticulous in his examination and so accurate in his diagnosis had been none other than the former British Director of Medical Services, Dr. Selwyn-Clarke, and that the dentist who had done such a magnificent job on his teeth was an eminent Chinese to whom he had been introduced by the same Selwyn-Clarke. These things he would have to keep until the next time he and Mitsuko were together. For the moment they had to stay locked up in his mind.

The letter, when he finished it, was a fine fat one. It would surely please Mitsuko, perhaps help to ease her worries.

About Miwa's suggestion, well it certainly was a sound one worth thinking about. He would leave it to themselves to decide, though his own advice would be to start working now towards an eventual move.

Kiyoshi (strange how the 'Uncle John' part of him seemed to temporarily cease to exist whenever he wrote to Mitsuko) closed and sealed his letter. His watch told him it was after midnight. There was no sound to be heard in the hospital.

*   *   *

'I did not come into personal contact with John Watanabe until January 1943 when I was admitted to Bowen Road suffering from amoebic dysentery and persistent attacks of malaria.

' "Watty", as we all knew him, was at this time interpreter to the Japanese Commandant. Although in no way secretive or surreptitious in his activities and, of course, at the greatest personal risk, Watty lost no opportunity of bringing comfort and showing kindness. This, in itself, in a place where no kindness was, was an act of mercy. His many little acts of service are too numerous to detail, but even a smile, a cheery word, a touch of the hand, under those circumstances, were like a blessing.

'On one occasion he asked me if I would write in his autograph album. Quite by chance, and probably because it was the only thing I could remember at the time, I wrote the words of the 16th Century Sussex prayer: "O Lord, support us all the day long of this troublous life". To my surprise, for at that time I did not know Watty was of the Christian faith, he appeared genuinely delighted.

'A little later he asked me to say what I would like to receive if I were given a wish. I replied that I should like to receive a letter from my wife. "Then," said Watty, "I think you should pray." I must explain that at this time no mail at all was being received, and I suspect that it was being destroyed at the Japanese H.Q.

'That night I was aroused by a movement under my pillow. Waking, I saw Watty going out of the room. I felt beneath my pillow and found 18 letters, all from my wife. I can think of no happier moment in my life, and from that time I began to make a rapid recovery. When I tried to thank him next day, Watty only smiled, shook his head, and pointed to the sky.

'During the time I was at Bowen Road, there was a secret radio operating in the building from which we received occasional news of the progress of the war. Not only would its discovery have resulted in torture and death for its operators, but, more serious still, undoubtedly the removal of even the meagre medical supplies available and, probably, the closure of the hospital.

'As the invasion of France began, it was arranged that, as the tame geographer of the outfit, I should record the progress of our forces on a map which I had drawn. Obviously this map was an extremely dangerous possession, and I made it a strict rule that it should never leave me. However, one day, most foolishly, I yielded to persuasion and lent it to a fellow officer to show to those in bed in another room. Unfortunately, when he went in, waving the map in his hand, a sentry stepped forward and took it from him.

'There followed several days of agonising suspense, presumably whilst the perpetrator of the map was being traced. At last, and almost with a sense of relief, I was told to go to the interrogation room. As usual on such occasions, I took my farewells of my friends and left messages for my wife, as all too often those taken for interrogation were not seen again.

'On entering the room I was astonished to find only Watty there. Heaven knows how he had persuaded the commandant to allow him to conduct the interrogation by himself. Watty was his usual serene self, and as he listened patiently to my carefully rehearsed tissue of lies, I knew with a sinking heart that it was impossible to lie to him, and that he knew the whole story.

'Then he said: "The commandant is very angry. He has told me to beat you with this belt until you tell the truth." He paused, and then he said: "I think it will be better if we are friends," and, taking my hand, he shook it.

'I asked him how he would arrange matters with the commandant. Watty replied: "I shall tell him you are an honest man and speak the truth." Then he added: "Perhaps you can help me and pretend you are in great pain from your beatings." Poor Watty—how he managed to persuade the commandant I shall never know. But I am sure that the falsehood he was obliged to utter on my behalf caused him more anxiety than anything else.

'I kept up the pantomime for a few days, and the matter was never referred to again except for a few jeers from the passing sentries. But there is no doubt that Watty saved my life and perhaps those of many others that day, for no one can say how long he can withold information when under torture.

'On another occasion—it was June 5th 1944 I remember— when the loudspeaker attached to the Japanese radio at Headquarters was blaring out its interminable programme of Japanese music, there was a sudden silence, and then the clear voice of the BBC announcer from London saying: 'This is London. Today Allied troops entered Rome." Another silence, and then the music started again.

'It is difficult to explain the effect that these few words could have upon us under those conditions, but it is a moment I shall never forget. Only Watanabe could have done it. Only Watanabe would have dared.

'And yet, in spite of all this, it would be quite wrong to assume that Watanabe was a traitor to his own country. He was in fact a most loyal Japanese who loved his people and his land. We were his enemies, but because we were his fellow men he loved us also.

'I remember talking to him once about the result of the war. "I think Japan will lose this war," he said. "But we are a patient people, and to wait another 100 years is as nothing to us."

There was nothing boastful or bitter in what he said, for such things were not possible in the man. He was speaking, as he always did, simply and from the heart.

'There was a serenity about him and in all that he did and said which could only have come from a mind completely at peace. I am convinced that, faced as he was with the terrible choice between obedience to his orders from men, and to those from his God, with all the shame, ignominy and physical suffering that the former could have brought him, he took his decision calmly and without hesitation.

'I have read of many great Christians. I have met only one— John Watanabe.'

Roger S. Rothwell,
(Formerly an Army Lieutenant
and inmate of Bowen Road)

*   *   *

The onward march of the Japanese forces in the Pacific slowed down, gradually came to a halt. Then, one day, they began to retreat. The Allied forces heaped on enormous pressures and drove the Japanese before them, and the myth of Japanese invincibility crumbled.

But in Hong Kong, as in many other occupied places like it, a true picture of how the war was progressing was impossible to get. Reports were carefully doctored, and all news bulletins carried a heavy leavening of propaganda. As the reverses became more serious, so the tempers of Japanese senior officers worsened. Cruelty increased once more, and food supplies became shorter.

For the umpteenth time Uncle John wondered where it would all end.

It was Sunday, and he was on his way to Pasco's in Ice House

Street. After his visit there, he intended going to see Nellie and her children. Now, more than ever before, the regular money he gave her out of his pay, and the little supplies of food he brought, were of great value.

Whenever he went to see her these days, the children took him completely for granted. In them he saw the reflections of his own children as they grew out of babyhood and started to develop their own personalities as little human beings. They knew him as nothing else other than 'Uncle John'. In their non-complex minds they were able to accept him purely and simply for what he was—a friend. They were not beset by any con-siderations of race, or politics or religious creed. He loved them as much as he admired the tenacity and courage of their mother.

Sometimes, in her rare quiet moods, Nellie would dissect all his actions and motives.

'I don't know how you do it, Uncle John,' she'd say. 'I mean the calm way you were able to walk into that camp carrying all that stuff. If you were caught...'

'But I wasn't caught, Nellie. You and Wendy and Junie and Barbie were my protectors.'

'Yeah, but even so—there was nothing impulsive about what you did. You know, you did it calculatedly, and you must have known what could have happened to you if they caught you. Weren't you ever scared?'

'Yes,' he said. 'Always I was afraid. I am a coward.'

'That's nonsense!' she said. 'How could you be a coward and still go on?'

'But that's where you make your mistake, Nellie,' Uncle John said, and he wished he could get this women to understand. 'Always you say you don't understand how I do it. I—I don't do anything.'

'What about Shamshui Po? The medicines, the messages to and from the prisoners? What about the Sun Wah Hotel and Bowen Road, and coming to see *me*, smuggling your food out? What about all these? How can you say you do nothing?'

Would he ever be able to make her understand? He leaned

towards her, and when he spoke, the urgency caused him to pucker his forehead into fierce wrinkles.

'It is not *me*, Nellie,' he said. 'I do nothing. It is God who does it. He only uses me. It is He who took the serum into Shamshui Po, but He got *me* to carry it. Do you understand?'

She didn't say anything, but nodded in that little-girl way of hers. He knew she half got what he was trying to tell her, but she didn't really understand.

He thought about going on, trying to explain at length to her. But there wasn't any more to explain. What he had said, he had meant implicitly. It had expressed precisely what he believed. So, in the end, he didn't say any more to Nellie Lee about it.

*   *   *

Colonel Tokunaga was alone, walking in the afternoon sun through the Victoria streets. Uncle John saw him from a long way off, from maybe a hundred and fifty yards. He couldn't help but see him, because the colonel stepped off the footpath on the far side of the street and crossed diagonally to Uncle John's side.

As the officer came towards him, Uncle John reflected that this was the first time he had met Colonel Tokunaga in the street. He was a little surprised that the other man was alone. He wondered where the officer was coming from, or where he was going. Of course he had often heard it said that Tokunaga, like so many other Japanese, had a 'Hong Kong wife'. He assumed now that the colonel was either going to or coming from a meeting with his woman.

The colonel didn't see Uncle John until both men were no further than a yard apart. Then Uncle John bowed from the waist and said: 'Good afternoon, Colonel.'

Tokunaga stopped and looked straight back at him without replying, then dropped his eyes to Uncle John's feet before bringing them back slowly up his body until he was looking at his face. He did not speak but turned away abruptly and continued walking.

Uncle John had an immediate foreboding of unpleasantness. Tomorrow, perhaps the next day, the colonel would send for him. Meanwhile, he had business to see to with Mr. Pasco.

While he was in Pasco's shop, a Chinese girl came in. Pasco called her over and introduced her to Uncle John.

'This is Miss Helen Ho,' Pasco said. 'She is one of the—eh—nameless ones who have been helping. Helen, this is Mr. Watanabe.'

The girl put out her hand and smiled shyly.

'Ah, Uncle John,' she said. 'Doctor Selwyn-Clarke has spoken about you.'

Uncle John too had heard of Helen Ho. Selwyn-Clarke had told him how, among other things, Helen made peanut butter in her own home for inclusion in the parcels for the prisoners of war. Uncle John understood she acted as tutor to Selwyn-Clarke's daughter. He looked upon her as a very faithful and brave person.

The three talked for some time, and then Uncle John took his leave of them. He was going to see Nellie. Today he was meeting her in the open air, at a spot on the hill high up above the harbour.

When he got to their rendezvous, he was early. He let his mind relax for a few moments and looked around. There was a strong scent of flowers in the air, and when he looked down towards the harbour, his eyes rejected the details, the squalor and the ugliness of the depressed places, and selected instead the finer things. There was a hush up here. War didn't exist. Only beauty. The two things were incompatible, and this was the time for beauty.

He looked towards the mainland, and again his eyes rejected, this time Kowloon. He looked beyond it to where the hills, purple in the distance, made an uneven saw-tooth pattern against the sky. And then he looked seawards, towards the islands. He knew it was fanciful to think this way, but on a few occasions he had found himself wondering if the scenery in Paradise might not be just a little like that of Hong Kong.

Pealing laughter suddenly cut in on him, and three children were running straight for him with arms outstretched. He turned, and there was Nellie too coming towards him shaking her head in mock admonishment.

'We caught you, you old dreamer!' she was saying. 'What were you dreaming of, eh? Come on, tell us, what were you dreaming of?'

'I was just thinking, Nellie,' he said.

Nellie said: 'I know you were thinking, I saw you. I tried to keep the children quiet so we could give you a surprise-surprise, you know, come right up on you. I told them, I said: "Hush now kids, there's old Uncle John dreaming away there. Let's give him a big surprise." But they couldn't keep it up. What were you dreaming of? Japan?'

He played with the children a while.

'I was thinking how beautiful this is, the scenery,' he said.

'Yeah,' she said, 'it is lovely, isn't it? But haven't you got nice scenery in Japan too?'

'Oh yes,' he answered, 'beautiful scenery. Many of us who live in Japan think that no more beautiful scenery than ours exists anywhere else in the world. In a way I suppose that is true. But our scenery is of only one type. It is island scenery, delicate and small and incredibly beautiful. But when I went to America, I saw majesty, Nellie. In the Grand Canyon, and in the great National Parks. Continental scenery, if I may put it that way. Here in Hong Kong I found another kind of beauty that I cannot describe. When you get away, even for a moment, from horror and the war and see only the views, it is ... it is like Paradise.'

He laughed a little from embarrassment. But Nellie didn't laugh. She was looking out over the harbour.

107

She looked too at this strange man who was bending over playing with her children, making them laugh.

She had grown to know him very well and felt a deep and lasting affection for him. It was the sort of affection a woman has for a father she adores. In Uncle John she came face to face with the sort of goodness that previously she had only read about, and though she was by no means an over-religious woman, she was convinced that the man was a saint.

She looked at him unobtrusively, smiled when he glanced at her, and thought of the times that tears of shame made his eyes glisten. She remembered the times he had come to her and told her of the poor ('the innocent ones' he had called them) being beaten until they bled.

'I know fuel is very scarce in Hong Kong, Nellie,' he had said, 'and every leaf is so precious. But when I see poor people with bundles of dried grass and twigs and leaves being hit by Japanese soldiers, I feel indignant. More than that—I feel ashamed.'

That was when he cried.

Recovered, he had said: 'And all I can do is pray that some human feelings will return. My people are crazy with war. They make no distinction between the combatants and the innocent. War makes my people mad, and I cry for my Japan.'

Later he said: 'You must think me a great fool for such behaviour.'

It all kaleidescoped across her mind as she stood looking at him now making her children laugh. She had never known anyone quite like him.

*　　*　　*

Over in Shamshui Po Camp, one of the many men who often wondered about the helpful interpreter who had been shifted was John N. Crawford, a doctor in the Canadian Army.

He remembered Uncle John as a 'very quiet, shy man. His Christian conviction made him a very brave man. I do not know what his fate might have been if he had been caught bringing medicines in to me for the use of my troops, but in all probability he would have been punished severely. The Japanese Kempeitai, or secret police, were very good at that sort of thing.

'I am sure that a great many Canadian troops owe their lives to Mr. Watanabe's bravery.'

Doctor Crawford remembered with a great deal of gratitude. He also wondered. He wondered whether Watanabe were dead or alive.

*   *   *

Whenever there was a funeral in Bowen Road Hospital, Uncle John attended. He did not have to resort to any sort of deception to do so, because he was now officially allowed to attend. He would stand a little way from Padre Squire (who had become a very good friend of his) and he soon knew the burial service off by heart.

But the effect that funerals had on him never lessened. When the first shovelful of earth thudded deep into the graves, he had to turn away, always. Even though in many instances death was a release from suffering, it did not fail to move him to think that a man had died, that physically he was no more. The words of the service burned themselves indelibly on to his brain.

It was after such a funeral that Colonel Tokunaga visited the hospital and sent for the interpreter.

'I saw you out in civilian clothes on Sunday, Watanabe,' he said. 'You should know men of non-commissioned-officer rank are NOT allowed out without uniform, at ANY time. I am sick of you. Your behaviour is not soldier-like. You are no good. You are just a ... a ...'

The colonel sought for the most insulting word he knew. When he found it, he said it with venom.

'You are just a filthy *civilian*!'

Uncle John, in his mind, concurred. Of course he was a civilian, and had been for over half a century.

He bowed to Colonel Tokunaga and said: 'Yes, sir, I am sorry sir.'

'Oh "sorry, sorry" what does that mean? You are always "sorry sir".'

Uncle John did one of his listening-without-hearing acts for the next three minutes while the colonel ranted and raved at him about military discipline. When the officer finished, Uncle John saluted and crept quietly out of the room before Tokunaga erupted again. He felt lucky to get away with a scolding. He waited until the colonel left, accompanied by Major Saito. Then he went out into one of the wards. There was a new patient in, a man named Ivor Gale from Shamshui Po Camp and Uncle John wanted to talk to him.

He asked Ivor Gale many questions about the camp across the water. He was able to get news of various people he had befriended there, and Gale appeared quite willing to answer as many questions as Uncle John cared to put to him.

Finally, Uncle John asked Ivor Gale the inevitable question— would he write something in the autograph book?

Gale answered 'Yes' instantly, then said: 'You remember Lieutenant Potter?'

The name was familiar, but Uncle John couldn't match it up with a face. Five thousand men were a lot from which to try and remember *one* face just like that.

Gale said: 'I'm sure you must remember him, Alan Potter, he was a lieutenant in the St. John's Ambulance Corps.'

This brought it back to Uncle John.

'Well,' Gale said, 'in May 1942, when he was still in Shamshui Po, Alan Potter wrote a poem about prison. In October the same year he left Shamshui Po to go to Japan on the *Lisbon Maru* which, as you probably know, was sunk with a loss of over 800 P.O.W.'s. If you don't mind, because I think it is beautiful, I would like to write Alan Potter's poem in your autograph book in memory of him.'

Uncle John said: 'I should be honoured if you would do so,' and he handed the book (now almost half full of signatures and messages and drawings) to Gale. When he got it back, the seven stanzas of Lieutenant Potter's poem were written neatly in purple ink. He read it many times that night. He thought it very beautiful. He was amazed that a man could still find beauty of thought and expression in such awful surroundings. Each time he read it, the tragic irony of it seemed more poignant.

My prison window opens out
Upon a vista wide,
An island studded harbour set
With hills on every side,
And right ahead, aye, calling me,
A passage to the open sea.

My prison house is fenced around
With lines of knotted wire,
And weapon'd guards keep vigil there
To foil my heart's desire.
'Tis naught, for fancy lets me free
Through yonder channel out to sea.

When morning breaks along the hills
And floods the bay with light,
I rise from my dream-haunted bed
And first direct my sight
Where running tide goes flowing free
Through that blest channel, out to sea.

And when the sun, a flaming ball,
Stoops Westward to his bed,
And Toing-I-Isle stands castle-like

Against the flaming red,
The sunset streamers beckon me
To sail that passage out to sea.

When night enshrouds the silent camp,
And slumber holds me fast,
'Midst all the dreams of distant ones
That conjure up the past,
The constant vision comes to me
Of that near channel out to sea.

Though comfort small this place affords,
My constant joy is found
In all the sweep of hills and bay
That rings the camp around.
And, for supremest luxury,
I have my passage out to sea.

In selfsame manner in our life:
In narrow limits cast,
In action cramped, with vision wide,
Our mortal days are passed.
But freedom for Eternity
Waits through that channel out to sea.

CHAPTER IX

Those who spent any time in Bowen Road Hospital had to contend with the one big bugbear with which all prisoners of war are confronted—boredom. In more leisured times, after the war, psychiatrists would be able to make pronouncements and write learned treatises on the effects that enforced inactivity can have on the human mind.

But, living in the middle of it, seeing it happen, Uncle John could not be detached. He was unable to stand back and merely objectively view. He felt himself implicated, and very often he saw men losing their grip on life and sanity because they were unfitted to deal with the frightening experience of doing nothing. Whenever possible, he encouraged the patients to take up some activity which would occupy their minds. Being a spectator at the degeneration of a human being was a gruesome experience.

The doctors, he noticed, were all the time trying to learn. Occasionally he was allowed to attend the post mortems held by the British doctors. Sometimes he was shown the specimens they preserved. The keenness of these doctors to keep their medical knowledge up to scratch and, where possible, to add to it, was in sharp contrast to the attitude of Major Saito.

The Japanese doctor seemed to have lost all love for his profession. It was, Uncle John thought, a shameful waste of a man's talents. Saito's new way of life owed nothing to Hippocrates. It was as if the man had undertaken a total rejection of his pledge as a doctor.

Of the patients, one of the senior officers, Lieutenant Colonel R. C. Rawlinson, took up sketching and, rightly or wrongly, Uncle John chose to look upon it as the colonel's sheet anchor which prevented his mind from drifting into the dangerous straits of lassitude.

He saw some of the sketches Colonel Rawlinson had managed to do with little more than a stub of pencil. The proportions were perfect, but the details were often crude because of the inadequacy of the Colonel's drawing equipment. Uncle John asked Rawlinson if there was anything he required. Rawlinson smiled wryly and reeled off a list of things ranging from soft and hard lead pencils to black Indian ink.

The man said his piece as if it were a challenge, as if he knew full well there was no chance of getting the materials. But Uncle John had other ideas. If this talented man needed these materials to keep his talent alive and his mind from the decay of disuse, then he, Uncle John, would have to be the provider.

It was through Mr. Pasco that the pencils and paper and ink were found, and Uncle John himself brought them in and laid them on Colonel Rawlinson's bed. The man seemed to hesitate before accepting them, and then, when he did, he immediately opened the package and took out its contents and stared in a sort of blatant disbelief. Again there was the searching for words of thanks. But Uncle John dismissed it by walking away. He knew how Rawlinson felt.

At night the hours dragged slowly for Uncle John. During the day he was at least able to crowd the minutes with things that had to be done. The bed-time hours provided no such respite. He lay in the darkness groping for a sleep which his racing mind staved off.

There were occasions when he wondered if the events which had engulfed him since he left Japan had really happened at all. What if all this were only a figment of his imagination? Or of the subconscious? He had known of people who had suffered

114

from delusions. Suppose none of this around him had happened, or was happening, and that the explanation was that he had, somehow, somewhere become deranged?

When he sat up in bed and, in the darkness, called: 'Mitsuko! Mitsuko!' and got no reply, he became frightened. It was necessary then to relinquish the half-hold on the dream theory; and with its relinquishment went some of the fear about being deranged.

But he couldn't help forming comparisons between the then and the now, between the interpreter who was an unwilling witness to savagery and bravery and dignity and depravity, and the Lutheran pastor going about his church duties in Japan; between the many awful sights and doings that pressed in on him here in Hong Kong, and the innocent and undemanding life that had been his and his family's on the seven islands that made up the city of Hiroshima. Could it be the same Kiyoshi Watanabe? More worrying, *would* he be the same Kiyoshi Watanabe when all this was finished—if God spared him to live?

Everything has changed. That is what he often thought as he lay in bed waiting for sleep: everything is changed. Even the papers that came in infrequently from Hiroshima, the Osaka *Asahi* and Hiroshima's own *Chugoku*—they were full of war, of the statistics of casualties inflicted and suffered, of ships sunk and planes shot down and enemy prisoners of war captured. Places he had never heard of before screamed at him from headlines, Bataan and Wake Island and Iwo Jima.

When he got to sleep, it was to be involved in another world of similar confusions where men still killed and were killed, and where nothing made any more sense than it did in the world of reality.

*   *   *

Rawlinson was deeply engrossed in his work, head bent down over the paper, a frown of concentration furrowing his brow. Uncle John approached him silently to see what it was he was drawing. Rawlinson didn't notice the interpreter for a few moments, and when he did look up the drawing was finished.

Uncle John said: 'It is very beautiful.'

Rawlinson said: 'What? Oh, this! I was only experimenting.'

'Please, may I see?' Uncle John asked, and he put out his hand for the drawing.

Rawlinson handed him the small rectangle of paper. Drawn on it, in wonderful detail, was part of the interior of a church. Uncle John gazed at it, breathless when he held it close to his eyes and saw the thousands of tiny pencil strokes which had been applied with so much loving care.

'This is wonderful,' he said to Colonel Rawlinson. 'What church is this?'

'Norwich Cathedal,' the officer answered.

'Nor ... Nor-ich? How do you spell? Where is this place?'

'Oh, it's one of those peculiar English pronunciations,' Rawlinson said. 'It is spelled N-O-R-W-I-C-H, but pronounced as if it were N-O-R-R-I-C-H. It's a town about 100 miles northeast of London, in a county called Norfolk.'

'I see,' Uncle John said. 'And this is how its church looks?'

Rawlinson moved uneasily in the bed. He said: 'Well, I hope the drawing gives some idea of how it looks. The high altar is superb and the apse of the cathedral is one of the most perfect examples of Norman architecture in the world. It was built in the thirteenth century.'

'Thirteenth century' echoed Uncle John.

'Yes, incredible isn't it? It's hardly been touched since. I wish you could see it, especially its arches. They are magnificent, so simple and ... oh I'm sorry, I—eh got rather carried away.'

'No please, don't stop,' Uncle John urged.

But Rawlinson would say no more. Uncle John asked him if he would do a drawing for the autograph book.

Rawlinson said: 'You can have that one if you wish. Not that I think it's much good.'

'Thank you very much,' Uncle John said. 'I will never be able to really see this church, but every time I look at your drawing, I will still be able to "see" as much of it as you have let me see. Please, you will sign it for me?'

Rawlinson took back the drawing and underneath printed, NORMAN APSE, NORWICH. He signed it R.C.R.

After that, whenever he saw the colonel making delicate pencil or pen strokes, Uncle John would think with wonder of this man who, in the midst of loneliness and ugliness and pain, could see beautiful things in his mind. Things remembered and cherished which he translated on to the oblongs of paper before him. Many times the drawings were of churches and in time the colonel did two more, in black ink, specially for Uncle John.

Both were of little churches nestling in the sunlight and shadows among trees. On one, the clock said five past three. The other was captioned DOVERIDGE CHURCH, DERBYSHIRE. They were both signed R.C.R., Lt. Col., P.O.W. '44.

When he gave them to Uncle John, Rawlinson also handed him a signed slip of paper which read: 'In kind remembrance of all the trouble you took in acquiring the necessary things to enable me to do these sketches. Yours, R. C. Rawlinson, Lt. Col.'

This was one of the tiny minority of nice things that happened. Unpleasantness was the norm. The thing that which made each a day a brother to the day before.

Saito was becoming more tyrannical and intolerant, and subjected his interpreter to all sorts of scorn. The man's medical knowledge also invested him with the capacity to inflict mental stresses of the kind which in future years would be termed brainwashing. He tried repeatedly to drive Uncle John to breaking point and beyond, and, when he failed, flew into mad rages in which he lost all dignity.

Uncle John was aware the war news was getting worse. He regretted it and worried more and more about Mitsuko.

But Saito took the war news personally and ranted and swore about the Americans and how they would eventually be crushed into the ground. He took to wearing a revolver, and to walking about with an exaggerated swagger which gave him the appearance of a cartoon martinet. He struck poses intended to inspire awe; instead they contrived only to make him look ridiculous.

The day the first American plane came over Saito went berserk. He was in his office signing some papers which Uncle John had placed before him. The drone of the plane's engine from far out over the sea grew steadily louder until finally Saito shoved the papers from him and bawled: 'Here, Watanabe, take these away'

Uncle John lifted the papers off the desk and went out. Almost simultaneously with Saito's next shout of baffled rage, he heard another voice faraway somewhere in the hospital.

'Hey, it's a Yank! D'ye hear me, it's a Yank!'

There was a silence then for a while broken only by the vague sounds of movement in the hospital and the noise of the approaching plane. It must have been directly overhead when suddenly three or four voices from a ward joined in excited shouts: 'It is! It's the Yanks!' 'They're here—they're coming!' 'The good old bloody Yanks! Hip hip—' and three times a huge concerted 'Hurrah!' rang through Bowen Road Hospital.

But against the bursts of cheering Uncle John also heard the wild screaming of Saito in his office.

He came out at a run, maniacal anger causing his bloodshot eyes to bulge frighteningly.

He was screaming: 'Stop them! Stop them, Watanabe, you imbecile!'

Hardly knowing what to expect now, Uncle John muttered out loud: '*Shu Jesusu awaremi tamai!* Our Lord Jesus have pity on us' and walked after the still screaming Saito.

Once, briefly, Saito turned back and shouted: 'What? What are you muttering, fool?' He didn't wait for an answer. It is hardly likely that he would have got one. He stamped through the wards yelling and screaming.

Uncle John, bringing up in the rear, could see Saito's neck bulging as the anger caused his throat to constrict.

'Who cheered? I want the man who started cheering! Translate, Watanabe. I want the man who started the cheering.'

A tight-lipped silence was all the answer Saito's request received. The men looked from one to the other. Could this man before them, screaming like this, be really a doctor? a major?

'Who was it?' Saito screamed. 'Admit it! Who was it? You will not deceive me. I will find out. Who was it?'

Nobody came forward. Saito ordered everyone on parade. He walked among them then, striking indiscriminately at them. Only the silence answered him.

When the rage spent itself, Saito walked weakly to his office, muttering his hate.

Uncle John had never seen anyone so angry. The experience was, to say the least, humiliating. He was sorry for the patients who had been struck in such a cowardly fashion, but their silence had a dignity about it which he found uplifting.

In the evening, when he sat down to write to Mitsuko, his mind was still full of the incident. On an impulse he broke his inflexible rule about keeping off descriptions of how things really were in Hong Kong. Sharing his feelings might ease the tensions of his mind.

He was describing Saito. 'He is more ready to injure than help,' he wrote. 'I do not understand it. He will injure anyone who expresses, however vaguely, any feelings against Japan— and it does not matter if the person is dying already.

'He is a doctor, but he has never attended a post mortem while I have been here. The British doctors spend a lot of time studying beri-beri and the effects of malnutrition. But not Saito. He is just interested in marching about with a revolver strapped on his side. All he has time for is swaggering about in that fashion. I do not understand it. But I cannot dislike or hate him. I only feel sorry for him. I pity him. He needs to be prayed for I think.'

Having written a lot of it out of his system, he sat back in the chair and rested. His relief was almost tangible, though the effort had left him with a drained-away feeling. And he still had to decide whether to send the letter or not. There were all sorts of dangers involved.

In the end he went and found some matches and burned the entire letter carefully until only a small mound of ash remained. This he took outside and left for the wind to disperse.

It meant he still had a letter to compose and write to Mitsuko. But he had no regrets about the burning. It was better this way. He had written what needed writing, and now he was purged and easy in his mind. The new letter would be simple. Just the same as all the previous ones he had sent.

Saito's complaints to Tokunaga resulted in Uncle John being sent for yet again. In the office at Prince Edward Road he waited while the colonel talked angrily on the phone with Saito. He caught the words 'Military Police' and 'confession' and 'dissatisfied' being used.

Then Tokunaga yelled: 'Watanabe!'

Uncle John went in. The colonel, the phone still at his ear, was in a foul temper. Uncle John had heard some of the prisoners of war referring to Tokunaga as 'The White Pig' and 'The Pig'. That was something that Uncle John disliked intensely, the likening of any human being to an animal. But as he looked at his senior officer now, he had to admit to himself that, in a temper, the colonel was most unpleasant to look at.

The phone being jammed down startled him.

'I'm not wasting any words on you. Major Saito is dissatisfied with you. He's sick of you. Get your stuff out of the hospital immediately. I'm moving you to Stanley Camp.'

As usual, Colonel Tokunaga was brief. Uncle John left the office. There was no transport available, so he had to walk all the way back down the full length of Nathan Road as far as the Peninsula Hotel, then turn right, and along to the Star Ferry pier.

For the first time he noticed that the Rising Sun flags were no longer crisp and proud. Everywhere he looked, the flags were limp, some were tattered, all looked faded. And it was this which impressed him most. The sun, which in the early days had looked so bright and red, now appeared as a pale dirty pink.

Was there a symbol somewhere in this? Was Japan's rising sun a thing of the past, and was it now setting ineffectually, devoid of customary glory, as the war continued to run against his country?

He was sure the answers were 'yes' and 'yes'. The sadness in him was reflex and, for a little while at least, uncontrollable.

CHAPTER X

In Hiroshima there was a steadily growing awareness that war was coming closer every day. Mitsuko Watanabe could feel the communal fear which sprang from the happenings and signs around her—the newspaper announcements about plans for fire lanes (in case the city was subjected to an incendiary raid), the notices about alarms and signals, the precautions that people were urged to take, the forming of local area committees, the talk of air raid defence, the designation of 'safe areas'.

On top of that there was the evidence of people trying to evacuate, and their panic at the lack of adequate transport. Sometimes Mitsuko went and walked through the places where she and Kiyoshi had often gone together before. She went to Asano Park and strolled through the trees, and sometimes she stopped and looked at an individual tree and admired it, and thought how permanent it looked, and how fine, and how useless and wasteful it would be if that tree were mutilated and destroyed.

She went and looked at the river Ota, and stood unthinking, letting her eyes drift with the flow of the water, then dragging them back a bit and letting the same thing happen over and over again. On Sakai bridge, and on Misasa bridge, she stood and looked downward at the water flowing along. Her mind went back to the last time she had walked in this place. It had been with Kiyoshi, the night he returned from America.

She tried to bring back the past by imagining, pretending Kiyoshi was alongside her. But it was a useless thing, this futile daydream. When she got afraid she whipped up an annoyance at herself and spoke mentally as if to someone else. 'This is stupid. It is no way for a middle-aged woman to behave.'

Even that only partly worked. She would have to be firm. 'Gambare! Gambare! Gambare, Mitsuko!' she repeated to herself, 'Be brave! Be brave! Be brave, Mitsuko!'

She wrote some of her thoughts to Kiyoshi in Hong Kong. Obviously much of what went into her letters was censored out long before they got to him, but nevertheless, his words of encouragement always calmed her down. Oh if only he were back with her, all this silly fear would be as nothing.

*　　*　　*

Stanley Camp's thousands of civilian internees took no notice of the day a new interpreter arrived. As far as they were concerned one Jap face was just like another, and most Japanese in war warranted little other than dislike, often hatred.

For the new interpreter, however, Stanley was a new experience. Here, for the first time, he was meeting with Western civilians living under conditions of imprisonment. He was aware that they were officially designated Internees, but so far as he could see, they were just like the other prisoners. Their freedom had been taken away, they had no money, they were forced to barter their most treasured personal possessions. One man, E. Walter Davies, who had been Crown Solicitor, swapped a gold tooth filling for two packets of cigarettes. Like many others, he lost weight. From being a tall well-built man, he fell away to an angular skeleton weighing under eight stone.

People who had rarely eaten rice except in an occasional curry or rice pudding, were forced to eat nothing but rice every meal

123

for years on end. Many of them became violently sick from the unaccustomed diet.

Women traded their wedding rings to get extra bits of food from the Formosan guards; men lay awake from three o'clock in the morning trying to coax grass to burn to boil the kettles of water; the old folk formed squads of kitchen guards to watch over the miserly rice supplies.

Some became mean and jealous, and small frictions had a tendency to develop into major issues. But on the whole the bankers and accountants and solicitors, the policemen and tradesmen and civil servants who had to exist within the confines of Stanley Camp were possessed of a spirit which would allow of no defeat.

Facing this heterogeneous mass of people for the first time made Uncle John's head pound. He had a completely new set of problems to face, new contacts to try and find, new risks to take.

It was tempting to toy with the idea of not bothering this time, of sticking to himself and not getting involved in other peoples' troubles. It would make life with Tokunaga much more tolerable, possibly even pleasant. It wouldn't entail being cruel or anything. Just minding his own business and doing his job strictly to the letter of the law. Nothing more.

The temptation was very strong.

But the sight of the children quickly restored Uncle John's sense of proportion. It hadn't occurred to him that Stanley would be peopled with children as well as adults. How typical of war, he thought, that children too should be victimised.

*　　*　　*

'...and then at Christmas 1944, Mr. Watanabe came to me and said he had heard the children were to have a carol service. I said

124

Yes, that was correct. He shyly asked if he might be allowed to attend. I didn't know quite what to answer because I was afraid of the effect that the presence of a Japanese in uniform might have on the children. However I discussed it with some of the other Sunday Primary School teachers, and we agreed that Mr. Watanabe could come. But we were still very much in doubt about the advisability of our decision.

'We needn't have worried. The children took to him straight away, and Mr. Watanabe stood there listening to their little voices. After the children's rendering of "Away In The Manger" he said he would like to sing for them. First he sang "Holy Night" in Japanese, and then a Japanese Christmas carol. After that he spoke, and he brought home to all of us present the true meaning of the Christmas Message. He said this was a time when all men and women and children all over the world should be together in thought because, regardless of skin-colour or race, Jesus is the same for all of us.

'There was something fantastic about the fact that it was a Japanese, one of our enemies, who, of all people, should be standing there telling us of Christmas. Some of us, especially those of us who had suffered deeply, felt very bitter about the Japanese, but he, on his own, helped to wipe out a lot of that bitterness. It was terribly moving to listen to him.'

Mrs. Winifred Penny,
(formerly an internee at
Stanley Camp, Hong Kong.)

*   *   *

Colonel Tokunaga was visiting the camp and he was in his office when the phone rang. He picked it up and answered it just as Uncle John came into the room.

Uncle John expected to be upbraided for not getting there faster to save the colonel from so menial a task as answering a telephone. Instead Tokunaga kept on talking, nodding his head and making notes on a pad. He said, 'Watanabe' once in the course of his conversation. This struck fear into the heart of the interpeter.

Tokunaga called Uncle John.

The colonel was smiling.

'Sit down, Watanabe, I have some good news for you.'

Uncle John distrusted this sudden friendliness.

'I didn't know you had a son in the army, Watanabe,' Tokunaga commenced.

'Oh yes sir, two sons in the army.'

'Mm—mm—did you know one of them might be coming through Hong Kong?'

Uncle John's heart started thumping. He wanted to say: When? How soon? Will I be able to see him?

He said: 'No sir, I did not know.'

Tokunaga beamed. 'Well, he's here already,' he said. He waited then for it to sink in.

Uncle John couldn't sit still any longer. 'Will I—' he began, but Tokunaga held up his hand for silence.

'Don't be so impatient. Yes, your son—Shinya is it?—is on board a ship in the harbour. He is on his way south. He got in touch with the prisoners of war office in Hong Kong and asked if you and he could meet.'

Uncle John fidgetted and wished Tokunaga would not stop every now and then like this. There was nothing for it but to try and hold his patience.

'Well, Watanabe,' Tokunaga went on, 'it has all been arranged. Although your son is not allowed to leave the ship, I have seen to it that you will be allowed to go aboard to see him.'

Uncle John felt like jumping up there and then and running out of the room and running all the way into the city to board a launch and get out to see Shinya.

But now Tokunaga was getting all pedantic and condescending and wallowing in the drama of the occasion.

'This is a very unique occasion,' he was saying. 'For a father and his son to meet each other in the field of battle is a rare occurrence. And to show you that the Imperial Japanese Army is not entirely without soul to comprehend these matters, you Watanabe, one of the two individuals at the core of this happening, will be given the rest of this day free, also tonight, and until noon tomorrow. Furthermore, my own personal car will take you to the quayside as soon as you are ready to leave.'

Uncle John couldn't believe his ears. Surely this was a trick. But there was no illusion about the way the colonel stood up and went out into the sunlight and bellowed for his driver. Uncle John, in case the thing would suddenly prove to be a dream, hardly thanked Tokunaga properly before dashing into the car and saying to the driver: 'I am ready! I am ready now, please will you hurry'

For once he took no notice of the poverty and the poor they passed in the car on the drive into the city. He was too full of excitement at the prospect of meeting Shinya.

When he got to the quayside, the launch hadn't come alongside yet. He looked at the transport lying at anchor out there in the bay. He played a little game with himself, trying to visualise Shinya, wondering if he were on deck now, scanning the waterfront for sight of his father. Maybe the boy had borrowed binoculars and was even now, at this moment, nudging someone and saying: 'Look, there's my father, on the quay, waiting for the launch. Yes, that's him. He's an interpreter. Too old for the army—but not so old.'

And then Uncle John was in the launch, wishing the engine would go faster and push the boat more speedily through the water towards the troop carrier, towards his son.

When they came alongside the vessel, he looked up at the sea of faces staring downwards. He longed to call out Shinya's name. But this was a time for dignity, and he held the shout in his throat. The ship towered high above the launch, and his neck began to pain from looking up so steeply. It was hard to distinguish one face from another at that distance, though once he thought Shinya waved, a small tentative thing. He waved. Three or four soldiers waved back.

At last he was aboard, and there was Shinya, grinning, hurrying towards him.

The two clasped each other tightly, wordless, unable and not wanting to talk.

Then Uncle John took half a pace back from Shinya though still holding his shoulders. He wanted to see his boy. No, Shinya hadn't changed. He was still the same Shinya. He looked smart and brave in his uniform. Uncle John was proud for a little while, standing there looking at him thinking, this is my son.

He stayed on the vessel with Shinya, and they talked late into the night, about the family, about the things that had happened in the intervening years, about Japan, and, inevitably, about war. Shinya didn't like war. The extent of his dislike for it came out as the hours wore on and the two talked in quiet undertones.

Before going to sleep Uncle John said: 'You know, Shinya, in a way I was afraid to meet you.'

'Afraid, father? Why should you be afraid of me?'

'No, not afraid of you, my son; afraid for you.'

Shinya was puzzled.

Uncle John said: 'I was afraid that the madness of war might have got into you too, Shinya. I am too old for it to affect me. But you are young, and the young are impressionable. But, thank God, it has left you untouched. I am more proud of you than ever, my son.'

Shinya said: 'It is no merit of mine, father. It is because I am a Christian, and I would not be that were it not for you and my mother.'

It was a nice compliment, and Uncle John was grateful for it; but he knew he couldn't accept it wholly. He had to put it into perspective.

128

He said: 'No my son. It is not because of myself, or your mother—it is because of God.'

They slept then for the few remaining hours of the night.

*   *   *

When the time came to say goodbye, Uncle John got it over quickly. He didn't want a scene, and he knew that anything protracted would upset both himself and Shinya. So he merely gave Shinya some fatherly advice and said that he hoped it would not be long before they were all together again in Takasho Street, Hiroshima.

But even while he was saying this, his mind was telling him that the hope was slender. There was the war, and that seemed far from finished, and victory for Japan seemed dubious; there was the possibility, even probability, that either himself, or Shinya, or Shigawo, involved in the war as they were, would be killed in battle; and even if they survived, who could say whether Mitsuko's school and home would still be there? These thoughts niggled at him while his mouth spoke of other things.

Shinya, during the farewell, was brave. He nodded at what his father said, took a deep breath when the parting came, and went to the side of the ship to watch the launch breasting the waves, taking his father further from him, back to the shore.

From the launch Uncle John kept his eyes on the spot where he last saw Shinya standing. The distance merged the faces into a series of featureless blobs. A few times he made token waving movements with his hand. He felt very miserable.

The ship, so massive when seen from alongside, got smaller as the distance increased. By the time Uncle John stepped ashore the ship looked small and insignificant out in the harbour.

On the quayside he stood by himself and looked back for a

few minutes. Strange that the distance nullified everything. Now the ship was only a thing, a shape. But the mind knew differently. The mind knew that on and in that shape were people, beings, entities with feelings. He looked at the Chinese who were passing by. They knew nothing of what he was thinking. They walked and thought and disregarded him, or, if they noticed him, saw him only as a Japanese in uniform.

He looked back again at the ship and tried to bring back the hours he had spent with Shinya. The ship was hardly half a mile away, but it looked as dead as a boy's toy. He walked in then and was absorbed in the anonymous streets with their anonymous faces. It seemed incomprehensible to him that he could have tumultuous emotional thoughts in his head, and yet, to these Chinese, he was only a face above a Japanese uniform.

When he looked back, from the hill, for the last time and saw the small speck that was Shinya's ship, the misery left him with the feeling that everything was pointless. There was no reason for anything, and all that went on might be in vain. Being sensitive worsened it. If he had been born feelingless, none of this depression would hurt. And for the moment, there was no forseeable succour. Just Stanley with its half-starved thousands clinging to life; and Tokunaga with his inevitable questions.

He answered the colonel perfunctorily, even managed to smile, and, as Tokunaga drew him out, began to enjoy again the memory of the visit to the ship. By the time the interview was over, he was feeling better. At least he had seen one of the family again, and had been reassured about Shinya's attitude to war.

But he must stop self-pity, he told himself. It was unworthy of someone who had been given so much. And besides, he wasn't the only one who had some sadness to suffer. There were others—right here on his doorstep. He must try to help, not indulge in all this self-pity.

So he shook it from himself and went out among the people with the, to him, so-strange names. He felt for the women who had to sleep on bare concrete floors, and the men who tried so hard to keep their spirits up. He talked to some, who at first were suspicious and reserved. But they warmed to him, and he got to know many of their names—Mrs. Vera Doughty and her husband, and Frank Angus and the Whitefields and Ida Montgomery, these and many, many others.

*　　*　　*

'Although he was not supposed to wander round the camp, John soon came and made contact again, and from time to time we would have a talk. It was on one such occasion that I asked him how he came to be Christian, and whether his family was Christian. He answered "It was only when I was 17 that I found Jesus." He then said naïvely: "I try hard to follow Jesus, but I do not always succeed." It was the humble way in which he spoke that conveyed something which will always be a memory very dear to me.

'While John was in Stanley, I was able to re-establish a verbal contact with Mrs. Odell, and to communicate names of people who died in Stanley. For some reason the Japanese seemed not to want such information to get out. But John could not see how it could harm the Japanese in any way if it did.

'The camp was certainly a happier place when John was around, and when, on my birthday in February 1945, he arrived suddenly in the dark of the night and called me out, producing from the folds of his cloak an open tin of meat stew which Sophie Odell had given him for me, it was a wonderful surprise after two years of nothing but rice.

'Soon after that I had a grapevine warning that John was being watched, and to be careful. I told John, and he just smiled, and shortly afterwards he disappeared from the camp. . . .

'For me John will always remain as an outstanding character

131

in a dark world to admire and look up to in his truly Christian spirit.'

H. W. Hawkins.

*   *   *

Uncle John was aware that today, some time, a prisoner was being released from Stanley Gaol prior to being sent over to one of the prison camps on Kowloon. He didn't know which prisoner it was to be and so, when the door opened, was completely unprepared for the shock he got.

At first Uncle John didn't recognise the man. He was tall and gaunt with sunken eyes and most of his face was covered by a beard. The hair on his head was snow white, and lines of pain were deeply etched into the ravaged face.

Uncle John stood looking in silence. He wondered why this poor creature should look so familiar, and then it came to him and it horrified him—it was Selwyn-Clarke.

Uncle John didn't think. He ran across the office floor and groped for the prisoner's hand. Selwyn-Clarke raised his right hand and gave it to Uncle John, and Uncle John took it. The doctor had become an old man, and then suddenly Uncle John couldn't bear to look at him. He turned away for an instant and rubbed his knuckles into his eyes to force out the tears that were suffusing them.

Nothing existed for him at that moment only the ghost of the man he looked upon as the finest human being he had ever met. When he turned back, he saw that Selwyn-Clarke was smiling.

The Englishman whispered: 'My dear Uncle John, how good it is to see you.'

Uncle John squeezed the thin hand again and again and shook his head. For a while he wasn't going to trust himself to speak. Why had they done this to Selwyn-Clarke? What had

132

they done? Had they stopped at *anything*? He could hardly believe his eyes at the change in the quiet doctor he loved as a brother. The man was entirely changed. Old and different and full of suffering. And yet he was smiling, actually smiling, pleased to see Uncle John; when he should have hated the sight of every Japanese face, he was showing pleasure that Uncle John was standing there in front of him holding his hand.

For the few minutes they were together, Uncle John did not know what he was saying. He wanted to express something to Selwyn-Clarke and didn't know what it was or where to begin. There was too much to say, and this wasn't the time to try. And yet he had to say *something*.

Selwyn-Clarke put a hand on his shoulder and said some comforting words but the very gentleness of what he said hurt all the more. Uncle John wished in a way that Selwyn-Clarke might strike *him* as a sort of revenge. But no, the doctor was actually trying to comfort him!

Then Selwyn-Clarke was taken out, and Uncle John realised for the first time that all this had gone on in the presence of Tokunaga who had stood and watched and never opened his mouth. But Uncle John didn't care any more about Tokunaga now. Let him do what he wanted to do.

Tokunaga did nothing. But there was an expression of supreme distaste on his face when he looked at Uncle John before leaving Stanley to go back to Prince Edward Road. The look did nothing to Uncle John. In all likelihood it meant that his days were now numbered. But God had helped him every time up to now. Surely He would help him in the end too.

* * *

The visits of the planes became more frequent. Clearly the aircraft were carrying out reconnaisance runs before the big attack began. Whenever Uncle John happened to be out of doors and the drone of an engine overhead made him look up, he wondered when the bombing would begin.

It was a strange sensation to watch the glistening speck up there in the sky, and to think that inside it there were human beings who were plotting and photographing and talking about Hong Kong. But it made him uneasy to imagine what it would be like when a whole flock of planes flew over and then dropped their bombs on a target that couldn't run away. Sometimes he sweated at the thought of being hit by a piece of flying jagged shrapnel. To be killed outright by an explosion wouldn't be too bad. Just a blinding flash, and then nothing. But to die a lingering death—that appalled him.

Mitsuko's letters were becoming more and more serious. They told of a solitary American plane which now passed over the city every morning, and of the frightening roar as the bombers rendezvoused over Lake Biwa before streaming off to launch their attack on another town or city.

She wrote of her concern about the two youngest girls, both now mobilised for war work. Kei wasn't even at home. She was living in a dormitory a good forty minutes away at the naval station at Kure. Mitsuko's fretting stole into her letters and worried Uncle John. He felt a little easier about Kimi. She at least was fairly close to her mother and had to travel only a short distance to and from her daily work.

Mitsuko told of Miwa's continued efforts to get them all out of Hiroshima and down to Kiyushu where Miwa herself, a recently qualified midwife, was working with Hidezi. But the big problems were still transport and the fact that the girls, like all students, had been mobilised.

Uncle John lived in an agony of fear in case the raids on Hiroshima started before the family got away. He wrote and told them he was praying constantly for them, and that they were to place their trust in God.

He was in the middle of writing one such letter when the sound of plane engines began to grow louder. As his eyes were aching, he took the opportunity to leave the table and go across to the window to see whether they were Japanese planes.

They were coming in very fast, and suddenly they were overhead and starting to peel off as they came down in roaring power dives. And then there was the sound, the shuddering Currrumph! of the first bomb. The attack had begun. Some impulse made him run out into the sunshine, and he stood openmouthed as three of the planes banked out over the sea and came in together, low, over the camp. From somewhere very close came the sharp crack of rifle fire, and when he looked he saw some of the guards firing after the planes.

The next time the planes came in, the guards were down on their knees waiting, their rifles ready. They fired ahead of the aircraft, and one of the planes swerved slightly off course. Firing at the planes like this was crazy, and Uncle John knew it. The camp was clearly marked as a prison camp and, if the airmen observed the rules of warfare, should not be bombed. But neither should the planes be shot at.

Uncle John tried to shout this, but was too late. The enraged pilot whose plane had been hit took his aircraft around in a tight turn, and the next time he came over the camp, he came in with machine guns blazing. The bullets hit the baked earth and threw up gouts of dust as the sentries and everyone else within sight ran madly for the shelter of the houses.

Uncle John came out from under the table; great palls of smoke were rising over the hill from the city. The noise of explosions came from quite close by as well as from far away. He prayed mentally for those who were being killed now this very instant. Over the hill, he knew, men and women and children were being maimed and ripped to shreds by the murderous metal and flying debris.

Mercifully the pilot who had strafed the camp did not return right away. But shortly afterwards a bomb landed on a house nearby, and when the smoke cleared away, sixteen people were found to have perished.

The planes came on many days after that, and the letters from

Hiroshima stopped. Often Uncle John took Mitsuko's last letter out and read it. He clung to the paragraph which said '... and we are hoping to have left Hiroshima by about the middle of July. But it depends on so many things.'

One day he saw one of the American planes being hit, and, since it was a clear day, he watched, through binoculars, the parachute opening and the pilot drifting down slowly. The boy was caught, Uncle John found out later, and even though he surrendered, was taken to the Naval Headquarters and shot. A miserable waste of life, and terrible disregard for the sanctity of the rules about prisoners of war—that was how Uncle John felt.

He didn't really care now any more who won the war, as long as it finished soon and the wanton murder ceased.

He persuaded Nellie to leave Hong Kong and go to Macao. She didn't want to go, but he pointed out to her that she had a duty to her children now. There was no more she could do in Hong Kong, and it would not be a brave thing to stay on.

Saying goodbye to her was hard, but she made it easier by taking it in a matter-of-fact sort of way. The children ran up to him.

'Say goodbye to Uncle John children,' Nellie said. It was the same thing she said every time they had met. But this time it was as if the children knew there was a permanence about it. They came to him and kissed him, and the two older ones clung to him in childish hugs.

He shook hands with Nellie.

'Goodbye, Uncle John,' she said.

Apart from an extra tight pressure of the hand, there was nothing about her to suggest that this might be the last time they would see each other.

Uncle John had to fight hard to keep from crying.

'God bless you, Nellie,' he said. He didn't trust himself to add to it.

What a brave little woman she is, he thought as he walked away from the four of them.

He had gone about thirty paces or so when he remembered something of great importance. He stopped.

'Nellie!' he called.

'Yes?' Nellie answered. 'Have you forgotten something?'

'Yes—please remind the children to pray for me!' he said. 'I shall need their help more than ever now.'

She nodded her head.

'Sure,' she said, 'I won't ever let them forget.'

He walked away then and tried hard to keep his head up. Every time he turned back, they were all standing waving after him. They didn't stop until he could no longer see them, nor they him.

It took him many hours to get over the depression that saying goodbye to them had brought on. He had grown very close to Nellie Lee and her little family.

The raids got worse and Uncle John's spirits sank. He couldn't get Mitsuko off his mind. Hiroshima must become a target any day now. Why was there no news? He had nothing to hold onto but the letter with its sentence '...and we are hoping to have left Hiroshima by about the middle of July'. He hoped to God they had got away.

* * *

Colonel Tokunaga's heels hit venomously into the floor as he half-ran from behind his desk. He came and stood with his face only inches from that of the interpreter. The colonel's eyes were bulging, his lips clenched tighly, and sweat had already beaded on his forehead and was beginning to run down his face. Without blinking or shifting his eyes from the interpreter, Tokunaga dabbed at the sweat with a soaked handkerchief.

For many seconds no word was spoken. The only sounds in the room came from the slowly revolving ceiling fan, and

Colonel Tokunaga's nose which was drawing in air in noisy hisses. The colonel's expression was a mixture of loathing and rage.

Interpreter Watanabe stood, weak with fear.

The fear had been building up since the call came, two hours before, summoning him to Prince Edward Road. Once he knew that it was the colonel who wanted him, Uncle John had begun to tremble. There was no controlling his emotions. A summons to Tokunaga's office could only mean the worst. And now here he was, feeling small and vulnerable before the wrath of a man who despised him and who had the power to command unspeakable things.

The colonel turned abruptly and walked halfway across the room where he hoicked and spat green-yellow phlegm on the floor.

'Haagh! You make me feel contaminated, Watanabe!' he said as he turned to face Uncle John. 'You make me feel unclean even *standing* near you. To call you swine would be to insult the pig. But you have reached the end of your road, Mister Lutheran Minister, because now I know all about you. I have all the proof that I need. I think that I was blinded to your treachery by my own softness and kindness! But no more, no, not any more. So you helped Doctor Selwyn-Clarke, did you? And you betrayed Japan? You defied orders, my orders, other officers' orders, and toadied to the British. I wonder what else you did.'

'I did not betray Japan, sir,' Uncle John began. 'I did not——'

'Silence!' Tokunaga roared. 'You *dare* contradict me, animal?' The colonel stopped talking for a few seconds, leaving a heavy oppressive silence. He did not once flick his eyes away from Watanabe. 'Where are your friends now Watanabe, eh? Will the eminent doctor come to your aid? Or the woman? Or the proud and haughty Europeans from Stanley Camp? Are they any good to you now? You were a fool—but a dangerous fool—and now you are a helpless old fool. And I'll tell you something else—you are going to die.' He paused again.

O sweet Jesus, help me! Uncle John silently implored.

'Doesn't that frighten you, Watanabe?' Tokunaga said. 'You're going to die. You are going to bleed and scream with pain, and nobody will pity you. What do you say now, Lutheran?'

Uncle John said nothing.

'It makes you afraid, doesn't it? You can't even talk. But it won't be sudden, Watanabe, and it won't be soon, because much as I should like to kill you myself, with my sword, I am leaving it in the hands of the Kempeitai. They will act when they are ready. They will follow you, and they will take you when you are demented with fear. And don't think of trying to escape. There *is* no escape from Hong Kong. Now get your miserable belongings and get out of Stanley Camp.'

'Where shall I go, sir?' Uncle John asked.

' "Where shall I go, sir" ' Tokunaga mimicked. 'Go to your friends and see how many of them want you. But get out of here now, and get out of Stanley Camp, and leave your uniform so that we can burn it. Scum, leave my office!'

Uncle John slipped out of the building not knowing what to do, which way to turn. With the Kempeitai on to him, there was nothing for him to do except wait. The secret police were, he knew, exceedingly clever and unbelievably vicious. He was puzzled about why he had been set free. Perhaps it was so that they could keep further watch on him in the hope that he would lead them to others.

He looked around to see if he was being followed. Was it imagination, or *had* someone slipped into a doorway? He walked on. Several times he stopped and pretended to look innocently into shop windows, but he was really trying to detect followers in the reflection. Had that man been there all the time? The one looking his way now?

How long would it be before the Kempeitai pounced? Surely it couldn't be too long, because the war was going badly. If the Americans kept up the pressure, Hong Kong would soon fall.

With a mind confused and reeling, he made his way to

Stanley Camp. The news of what Tokunaga had said to him had got there before him, and he was thumped and hit and spat at by the camp personnel before he finally left the place.

Now he was on his own in Hong Kong, reviled by his fellow men, sentenced to death by the secret police, detested by the Chinese and (as it several times seemed) rejected by his God.

Time, as it had on a number of occasions in the past, blurred so that he had no idea of day or night, no memory of detail, no inclination to eat, no conscious awareness of where he slept or stayed. Once he thought he knew what Gethsemane must have been like, but felt a hot flush of shame at his presumption.

Some people must have helped him, this he knew. Who they were, he did not know. He lay down and tried to sleep. But where it was he lay, he did not know. Vaguely he was aware that his mind and his emotions were being bombarded, and that somehow he was existing with fear and confusion always at his shoulder.

*   *   *

Uncle John lay awake. It was stiflingly hot, and no matter which way he turned he couldn't stay cool enough to drop off to sleep. Always, within minutes, he was sweating again. The sheets and pillow were smelling badly, and when he drew breath, the hot muggy air made him gasp for more breath.

A couple of mosquitoes had somehow got inside his net, and again and again, when it seemed as if sleep might be attained, they swooped, buzzing noisily, near his head. Several times, when they bit, or he fancied the tickle that itched was due to one of them landing on his body, he slapped hard and suddenly, hoping to kill them. He gave it up after a while. The insects were too quick for him. There could be no sleep.

Once he did doze off for a brief few minutes, but he woke,

terrified, in a nightmare in which he and Mitsuko were involved in some nameless hopeless struggle. He lay back again and tried to push the vision of Mitsuko out of his mind. He even tried talking out loud about other things—anything that might drive his mind away from Hiroshima and Takasho Street. But, in the middle of a sentence, he found his words drying up as his mind kept drawing on thoughts of his wife.

Finally he abandoned the effort to drive Mitsuko from his thoughts. He gave himself to the other thoughts.

He allowed the whole mass of doubts and facts and fears to pour in, undiciplined; he hoped this would, in some way, purge him and when it was over, leave him easier in mind.

It was horrifying as it was happening. Three or four recurrent fear-thoughts hammered in his brain. They came back repeatedly, pierced in and stunned. And when the torment eased, they came again, repeating the process. There was so much he knew about Hiroshima; and also so much he didn't know.

The silence of Mitsuko was awful. From her, and from the newspapers and bulletins, he knew that Hiroshima had only twice been attacked—once in March when a couple of light bombs had been dropped, and once by a single raider which dumped about a dozen heavier bombs indiscriminately on the city. But there was something peculiar, something frightening about the Americans' failure to attack this huge city of 300,000 people. And something sinister about the single plane which, Mitsuko said, came over one morning and did nothing. It was as if Hiroshima were being singled out for something disastrous.

Mitsuko had told him of the closed shops, the shortage of food, the terrible silence of the city, the people trying to stream out, and being turned back at the boundaries because they hadn't got the authorities' permission to leave.

And yet Hiroshima was being spared while other cities were attacked. It made no sense; or rather it *did*, to him, because the failure of the Americans to bomb it seemed uncommonly like a deliberate saving of the place for an all out massive raid.

When he thought of the possibility of Mitsuko dying without

his ever being able to see her again, he turned his head into the pillow and wept without shame or restaint. There was nobody who could help him or help Mitsuko. There was only the Almighty. When he regained his composure he chided himself for thinking of God as 'only'.

He got up and, remembering that he was a Lutheran Pastor, prayed for strength and guidance; and he prayed for his family, particularly for his wife and two daughters in Hiroshima. He asked that they be allowed to get away from the city, to get clear outside Hiroshima, or to Hatsukaichi in the Southwest. Lastly he prayed for anyone else who might need prayers this night and on the day that was coming.

*　　*　　*

In a hut on the Pacific Island of Tinian, a young chaplain was standing before a group of men. In less than a couple of hours from now these men would be flying off the coral runway and into the night sky. Their planes had other names, apart from the maker's classification.

There was the 'Great Artiste' and the 'Full House' and 'Jabbit III' and the 'Straight Flush'. And there was another plane, the most important of the lot, and she was called 'Enola Gay'. In Enola Gay's bomb bay was a fat stumpy bomb called 'Little Boy'.

The crews of these aeroplanes, and of No. 91, the photography plane that was to go on their mission with them, were listening to the chaplain. He was praying. He said: 'We pray Thee that the end of the war may come soon, and that once more we may know peace on earth. May the men who fly this night be kept safe in Thy care, and may they be returned safely to us. We shall go forward trusting in Thee, knowing that we are in Thy care now and forever. In the name of Jesus Christ, Amen.'

The chaplain's name was William B. Downey. Like Kiyoshi Watanabe, he too was a Lutheran. The date was August 5, 1945.

*   *   *

In Hiroshima, Mitsuko Watanabe's school in Takasho Street had been affected only slightly by the evacuation. She was waiting for clearance for herself and Kimi and Kei to get to Kyushu, but she was worried about Kei having to work over in Kure. A naval depot, that was sure to be one of the first targets when the bombing began. Mitsuko would be glad when she could shut down the school and get away to Hidezi's place.

There had been no word from Kiyoshi for some weeks. Perhaps tomorrow would bring a letter.

*   *   *

At 7.17 a.m. on Monday August 6th 1945, one of the aircraft from Tinian was six miles over Hiroshima. It was 'Straight Flush'.

Her wireless operator sent out a weather report to the plane carrying the stumpy fat bomb 'Little Boy'.

Aboard 'Enola Gay', it was the last part of the message which, in a way, was the most important. It said: 'Advice; Bomb Primary.'

And so, precisely 61 minutes later, from a height of 31,600 feet, and from a position 3 miles East of the city, the fat stumpy bomb, 'Little Boy', fell from the underbelly of 'Enola Gay' and dropped in free flight towards Hiroshima. At that moment, *hardly any of the city's population were in air raid shelters. This was an atomic bomb attack, the first one ever.*

*　　*　　*

On August 7, 1945 Uncle John was sitting close to a wireless listening for any mention of Hiroshima. He had been doing this for days on end, ever since his anxiety had grown to the uncontrollable stage. All he had ever picked up were snippets of information which, though they told him nothing specific, at least put his mind at ease. None mentioned air attacks on the city.

Now, however, his stomach suddenly tightened with sickness. He strained his ears so as not to miss a word.

'A small number of B-29's penetrated into Hiroshima City a little after 8 a.m. yesterday morning and dropped a small number of bombs,' the announcer said. 'As a result, a considerable number of homes were reduced to ashes, and fires broke out in various parts of the city....'

Uncle John's mind blanked and he didn't hear the next few lines. He was shaking all over as a cold fear gripped him. This was the sort of news he had been waiting for and dreading.

'...enemy has exposed his cold-bloodedness and atrocious nature more and more in killing innocent people by the use of this new-type bomb....'

The announcer's voice came and went in spasms. Uncle John didn't know whether it was because of the poor reception, or because of his own sporadic periods of lucidity.

'...but as long as we formulate strong steel-like measures to cope with this type of bomb, it will be possible to keep the damage at a minimum. We must be careful at all times so that we will not fall victim to the enemy's machinations.'

144

He clicked off the wireless. He could listen to no more.

*   *   *

On his mind now all the time was the perpetual wondering about Hiroshima. He was frightened by the continued silence. He wanted a letter, a note from Mitsuko or one of the girls. Anything as long as it was an indication that all was well. He got no letter, no note.

Hong Kong suffered now as it had never suffered before. American Navy planes punished it severely, and the smell of burning hung everywhere on the dust-laden air. The senses boggled at the noise and chaos. Men, highly trained, did their human best to kill or maim their fellow men, and the young and the middle-aged and the old died all manner of deaths on the streets, in their houses, in the hospitals. Uncle John, on the verge of being old, led a sort of stupified existence through the worst of it.

It once occurred to him that he was being saved for something. Sometimes he was bewildered; at other times depressed; but he remained sensitive to all the assaults to which his perception laid him open.

He didn't want Japan to lose the war because he still loved her deeply. It was inconceivable that she should be humbled, and he was fully prepared to die for her. But he wanted to hear just once more from Mitsuko.

As soon as the capacity to again think straight returned to him, he went to the Red Cross people and told them his plight. He left his name and said he was hoping to receive a letter which might be re-addressed from Interpreter Watanabe to Rev. Kiyoshi Watanabe. At least that's what he hoped they would do at the Prison Camp administration offices.

He found it hard to convince himself that they would bother, but knew his sanity depended upon clutching such straws of hope. The pressures were there all the time. An outcast from his own people, he had begun to dodge any Japanese he encountered in the streets. He lived furtively, permanently frightened, always waiting for the hand on his arm which would mean the end of his 'freedom', the beginning of the Kempeitai-style death. As he repeatedly told himself, death itself was nothing to worry about; it was the preliminaries that scared him. And there was the continual threat of being beaten up by the Chinese before ever the secret police got him.

Even when he met Mr. Makimura and was offered a job, Uncle John thought it was a trap. But Makimura, a kindly and sincere man, gave him confidence, told him that he (Makimura) needed an interpreter and that he would be pleased to employ him on behalf of the Japanese Hong Kong Government. And so it was that, along with many other Japanese men, Uncle John heard the Emperor's momentous broadcast of August 15, 1945. This was the broadcast in which the Emperor spoke to his people and told them of the decision that had been reached. The war was over. Japan had surrendered to the enemy. Uncle John wept.

*   *   *

With the others, Uncle John was interned. Even behind wire he was treated as a pariah, and in his aloneness he could think of nothing other than Hiroshima. There was still a huge vagueness about exactly what had happened. It began to seep into Uncle John's mind that perhaps his family no longer existed. There were rumours about a strange bomb, and about the near-total destruction of Hiroshima and Nagasaki. Rumours and more rumours, but no official confirmation.

Strange, when the possibility occurred to him that Mitsuko

146

and the two youngsters might be dead, it came calmly to him. He didn't break down or feel emotional. He just thought about it, then talked to God and asked, as he had done so many thousands of times throughout his life, for help.

After all, there was still the *possibility* that the family had been able to leave for the country before Hiroshima had been attacked. He held desperately to this thought.

He was sitting alone one afternoon in the prison compound when two Allied soldiers came for him. 'Come on, Watanabe,' one of them said curtly. 'You're wanted. Gather your stuff and come with us.'

Uncle John, as he gathered up the few personal things he'd managed to hold on to, wondered what he was wanted for. Had he done wrong? Could it be the Kempeitai at last had come for him? But that was stupid. This was a British, or Allied, prisoner of war camp now, and the Kempeitai had no authority here. Used as he was to summonses which meant abuse, he went along with the soldiers in an apprehensive frame of mind.

He recognised the route they took, but couldn't figure out why they should be taking him to Kowloon Hospital. Perhaps it was to act as a padre. But surely they would have their own padres.

'Hold on here a moment, Jock,' one of the soldiers said. 'I'll go and see if they're ready to see this little bastard.'

He was back within seconds.

'I don't know why the heck they're bothering with you mate, I'll tell you that,' the soldier said to Uncle John. 'Come on, move'

They went along a passageway, stopped outside a closed door on which the soldier named Jock knocked, and immediately heard someone say: 'Come in.'

'In you go,' Jock said, opened the door, and gave Uncle John a small shove.

The man inside was already standing. He was gaunt, white-haired and smiling. There was no mistaking these eyes, that voice which had softly said: 'Come in,' but which now remained silent.

Uncle John's eyes filled with tears at the sight of Selwyn-Clarke. The two men embraced and stood there, quite wordless, in the centre of the floor. The tears poured unchecked down Uncle John's face. Enemies, the records said they were; their love and respect for each other wrote a powerful contradiction to the records.

When Selwyn-Clarke at last broke the silence he said: 'Well, Uncle John,' (his voice was still gentle, and he retained the 'Uncle John', shelving formality). 'Well, Uncle John, it's a strange world isn't it? I feel sad to think this is probably the last time we shall meet. I shall be going back to England shortly, and after that—who knows? But whatever happens, wherever I go, I'll remember you warmly as a remarkable friend.'

He bent down and picked up a letter which he held in his hand.

'I will try to see to it that you are treated well, Uncle John,' he went on. 'They will need you as an interpreter. And I'd like you to take this—' he handed the envelope to Uncle John—'as I think it may help you. I hope to see you again before I leave, but in case I don't, please accept my heartfelt thanks for everything. God bless you.'

Uncle John said goodbye. The sadness he felt at the parting was as much as he would have felt were the doctor his own true blood brother.

Afterwards he opened the letter. He read:

'To whom it may concern:

Mr. John K. Watanabe, Interpreter, formerly in Japanese Military Headquarters, Kowloon, and latterly in the Foreign Affairs Section of the Japanese Governor's Office, rendered valuable service during the Japanese occupation of Hong Kong.

At risk to his own life and liberty, he assisted me up to the time of my arrest by the Gendarmerie by taking in essential diphtheria antitoxin, drugs, vitamins and funds to enable the special diet kitchen to function.

He gave splendid service to the Military Hospital, Bowen Road, and later to those interned in Stanley Camp. He suffered at the hands of the Japanese Military for having humanitarian principles.

Any assistance that can be given him will be appreciated by the undersigned, who owes so much to Mr. Watanabe for his courageous and Christianlike attitude.

P. S. Selwyn-Clarke,
Director of Medical and
Sanitary Services, Hong Kong.

Uncle John read it over many times and then folded it carefully and placed it in an inside pocket. He treasured it almost as much as one of Mitsuko's letters.

They gave him a job at Kowloon Hospital and, as Selwyn-Clarke had promised, he was treated civilly and well. Any unpleasantness that did arise came either from former P.O.W.'s who, during their imprisonment, came to despise all things and people Japanese; or from those Japanese who still despised anyone who worked in close contact with 'the enemy'.

But one day a former internee with no hatred turned up. She was Mrs. Vera Doughty, a woman he had helped in Stanley Camp. Released, she had immediately started looking for 'the interpreter who had acted like a human being and who treated us like human beings'. Tracking him down to Kowloon Hospital, she extended an open invitation to him to visit herself and her husband at any time in their flat in Cameron Road.

Uncle John became a regular visitor at the Doughty home. He listened to their talk and sometimes joined in. They were exultant naturally at the way the war had gone—an exultation he could not share. They were kind to him, and he appreciated their kindness. Vera Doughty said he was a saint, and, unintentionally he became angry. How cheaply people used and

149

gave accolades like that, he said. Did they really *know* what a saint was? What it *really* meant to have been a saint?

Vera Doughty worried about him. He was visibly failing before their eyes. And then one night it all came out in a flood of emotion, all his pent-up concern about what had happened to his family the morning the Americans had dropped what the Japanese radio announcer had called 'the new-type bomb'.

'I *must* know soon, Mrs. Doughty,' he said. 'Otherwise I shall become mad. All this time and I have heard nothing. I cannot sleep at night because I do not know whether I should be happy or sorrowful. Where is my wife? Where are Kimi and Kei and Miwa? What can I do? What can I do, Mrs. Doughty? Tell me something that I can do. Please, Mrs. Doughty.'

What could Mrs. Doughty say?

During his off-duty hours, he worked tirelessly to get news of Mitsuko. He began to haunt the Red Cross branch office, and the Swiss representative got to know well the face of the little English-speaking Japanese interpreter.

But for Uncle John, there was never any news other than : NO TRACE. He wanted to write, but had nowhere to write to because his letters were never answered.

Often he sat talking to the Doughtys for hours, and he told them all about his family. Though they tried to give him hope, their faces betrayed their real feelings. They knew Hiroshima had been wiped out; the centre of the fire ball which resulted when 'Little Boy' exploded had had a temperature of one hundred million degrees; about 80,000 people had died, many of them ceasing to exist in any form other than a shadow burned into the ground. How then could Uncle John *really* hope?

But he did. He refused to relinquish the faint glimmerings. And still there was the strange calmness inside him, almost as if his subconscious had been prepared. When he prayed, he left everything in God's hands. He said: 'I need your strength. Please hear my cry to Thee.'

Then, one day, a naval officer visited the Doughtys, and when he mentioned he was going to Kure, Uncle John immediately asked him a great favour.

Uncle John said: 'Please, if you are going to Kure, would you please do something for me? My daughter was working there before the bomb came. Perhaps you would try to find her and ask her to write to me?'

The naval man said he would try, but pointed out that there would probably be thousands of similar enquiries being taken care of, and that Watanabe wasn't exactly an uncommon name in Japan. On top of that, the naval man said, he wasn't sure when he would be back in Hong Kong again. However, Uncle John pressed him gently. There was still a chance, a very slim chance.

Later that day Mrs. Doughty said: 'You know that letter Dr. Selwyn-Clarke gave you? I think you should have some copies made of it. You might lose the original. Get somebody in the office to type a few copies.'

Uncle John thought Mrs. Doughty was being tactful and trying to take his mind off Hiroshima. Nevertheless, the next morning, he gave Selwyn-Clarke's letter to a typist and had four copies made. These he showed Mrs. Doughty. She seemed pleased he had accepted her advice, and she put the copies away for him in safe keeping.

Two nights later, on his way home, he had just come to a dark part of the footpath when three or four shadowy figures closed in on him. He instinctively knew they were going to attack him, but before he could run, he received a stunning blow from something hard and metallic on the back of the head. As his knees crumbled, other blows rained on his shoulders and back. He thought, so this is the way I am to die—I am to be kicked to death. The boots crushed into his back and stomach; he heard his own voice, detached-sounding, crying out with pain. No more than an occasional word was spoken by his attackers. It was in Chinese, and Uncle John didn't understand any of what was said.

151

Then the blows stopped, and he was roughly turned over on to his back. His attackers began to go through his pockets. They took out his photographs, his pen, then his money. All these were thrown on the ground. Then the men went for the inside pockets, fished out his letters. There was a half-shout as they found what they were looking for, and he heard the sound of paper being ripped.

They left him then.

Uncle John's body screamed with pain. Blood poured from his mouth and from a gash behind his left ear. As he pulled himself up to see the men who had beaten him up, he saw a small group of men in British army uniforms emerging from the shadows down the road. They joined the Chinese who had beaten him and money changed hands. The two groups split up then.

Uncle John gathered up his scattered belongings. Back in his room, he checked through them. Everything was there—except Selwyn-Clarke's original letter. Nothing else was missing.

Uncle John couldn't understand. He was hurt and puzzled. Hurt in his heart as well as body. He tried to banish the hurt from his heart as quickly as possible. Otherwise, he knew, he ran the risk of growing to hate. The best thing was to try to understand. And even if full understanding was impossible, he must at least forgive. Those men have suffered much, he thought; perhaps revenge to them is purely instinctive; perhaps it is necessary.

From then on, he was careful where he walked.

Frequently he wondered about Nellie Lee, and whether she and her children were all right. He wondered whether Frank had lived through to the end, and whether they were all together now. He thought of the children on their knees asking for protection for their Uncle John. The image gave him a warm lonely feeling inside.

Then, one day, he got a little note. It was written on both sides of a tiny page, on war-time brown paper, and it had been hastily scribbled in indelible pencil.

'Dear Uncle John,

Came around to see you—at last we're going away—to Canada first, then to the States—leaving tomorrow morning —so very sorry to have missed you I will write you as soon as we're settled—we don't know exactly where we're going.

Lots of luck to you and a happy reunion with your family. I won't forget you—neither will the children—you were very good to us——

You're a swell person—I'll always think so.

We might see you again some day.

Sincerely,
Nellie & Frank and the kids.'

So the Lees were once more a whole family! Uncle John felt very happy for them. Nellie deserved this, she had been such a brave woman, the bravest woman he had ever known. And in the middle of her joy, she had remembered to wish him a happy reunion with *his* family.

The following day he went again to the Red Cross office. He left it seconds after arriving there. No news. No trace. On his way to work, he saw some of the ex-prisoners from Shamshui Po making for the go-downs where the ships were moored ready for the long voyage back to England.

Some of the men waved to him, those who recognised him, and he too recognised a few familiar faces. All of them looked happy. They were going home, back to wives and mothers and families.

A few shouted ugly remarks and called him 'little yellow bastard' as they passed. Of these he took no notice. They were entitled to their taunts. They had suffered. Now they were free, and they were on the side of the victors, and that was important to remember.

They were all going home. And Uncle John was staying behind; but eventually he too would be going, back out through Lyemun Gap, the way he had come in. But this time there would be no Rising Sun flags—only Stars and Stripes and Union Jacks.

*　　*　　*

Mrs. Doughty gave the letter to Uncle John. The naval officer had come back.

'Here you are,' Mrs. Doughty said. 'I think you should go to your room to read this.'

Uncle John thanked her and went into his room, closing the door behind him. He sat down on his bed and held the letter in front of him, fingering it, fidgeting, trying to pluck up courage to open it. He closed his eyes a moment and tried to picture how it would be if the letter told him the worst.

This was a moment of aloneness, of remoteness, like the moments of 1942 when he had had to pass the sentry carrying the medical equipment for the camp. Nobody could be with him. Whatever the letter said, it was for him and nobody else to suffer or enjoy, and the sooner he faced up to it the better.

In the end, when he could think of no other excuses for delaying, he took a deep breath, opened the envelope and began to read. He read it right through to the end, right down to Kimi's signature. Then he cried as he had cried few times in his life.

The last hope was gone. The letter, simply and starkly, in the language of a heart-broken schoolgirl to her father, told what had happened. How Miwa had come up from Kyushu to collect the family and was at home in Takasho Street on that morning of August 6; Miwa, the eldest, the proud young midwife.

Just as the bomb 'Little Boy' exploded, Kimi herself was arriving at the factory at Mukainada where she worked. Kei was in Kure. And then, in an instant, Hiroshima was decimated as the brilliant flash announced to the world that man, in his capacity to destroy, had surpassed himself.

154

The wife of Uncle John, of Kiyoshi Watanabe, the little boy from Nanataki who had grown to be a Lutheran pastor and then got caught in the barbarity of a world war, died that morning in Takasho Street. Her step daughter Miwa died with her.

Uncle John collapsed with grief, utterly broken now that the frightful climax had come. He thought of Kimi's description of how she had come into the smoking stench-filled desert that had been Hiroshima. She was looking for her mother and Miwa, and didn't know where to begin. She picked her way among the dead and dying, asking all the time if anyone had seen her mother.

Nobody had, and she turned hundreds of dead bodies over to look at their faces to see if she might find the ones she was looking for. Pathetic wrecks of humanity moaned and screamed amid the debris. There were calls of 'Tasukete Kure! Help, Please!' and 'Sensei! Doctor!' and 'Tasukete! Help! Itai! It hurts!' and many cries of 'Mizu! Mizu! Water! Water!'

But there was no Mitsuko, no mother for Kimi to find. Takasho Street didn't exist any more. There was only a flatness with rubble and dying and dead people. And presently Kimi had found a woman, a neighbour, burned badly and dying, and this woman had said: 'No, I did not see your mother, but I heard her. Immediately after the great light, when I was running away, I heard her calling out "Wait! Please wait for me!" That was all. But of course I could not wait. I had to run. I had to escape. You understand? Don't you? I had to escape.'

That woman escaped dying in Takasho Street. She died in another place two hours after Kimi talked to her.

Of Miwa there was no word, no sign. She had vanished without trace.

Afterwards, Kimi had picked her way through the rubble until she found the place where Takasho Street had been. She tried to estimate where their own house had stood. She stood there for a moment blank-minded, dull, lost in shock. Before she left, she picked up the only souvenir she could identify, the

155

fitting of her mother's handbag. There was no other thing she wanted.

On his bed, Uncle John felt abandoned in his grief. His mind went back to his early days as a pastor—not to the time of joy, but to the heartbreak on the day his little daughters died. Then into his mind came the face of his beloved Shigaru, the face of a woman who stopped smiling because her life had ebbed away. He thought too of Mitsuko, gentle Mitsuko who had come into his life and lifted the sadness out of it. And now she too had been taken, together with another of his daughters, Miwa. How much more would be asked of him?

He turned towards the wall, and the place on his ribs where he had been kicked ached. Father, Father, why hast Thou forsaken me? He lost all sense of time and slept intermittently. He wanted to pray, and he couldn't. For two days and two nights he lived with his sorrow, and then, bit by bit, he grew to accept and to understand and to forgive, until there was nothing more left to accept or understand, or forgive.

Then he got up and was calm. He prayed, washed himself and shaved, and went back to work.

God had taken almost every single thing he loved. But, Uncle John thought, I am *His* creature. I must do *His* will. He has been good to me, and who am I to question His will? If Mitsuko had to die, and Miwa with her, it is not for Kiyoshi Watanabe to say Why?

He totally accepted what had happened.

*   *   *

A year later, in a train passing through Hiroshima, a Japanese clergyman sat looking out of the window. He saw, for the first time since 1941, the city where he had lived. This was what Kimi had written about in a letter he had long since lost. He

156

saw where the bomb had made a desert with burned trees. Somewhere, in there, in the middle of it, was a shadow, or some dust, that had once been his wife.

When he was eventually able to go back, he went to the place where Takasho Street had been. He let the memories flit through his mind, and at the space where a certain house had stood, he paused to pick up a piece of burned metal, all that remained of a sewing machine.

Then he turned and made his way out again through the wasteland.

He would like to have stayed longer, but time was precious. There was much to be done, many people who needed help. 'You can still be useful, Uncle John,' he said aloud. And he smiled a small smile at his own voice saying the name Uncle John.

POSTSCRIPT

by

Sir Selwyn Selwyn-Clarke, K.B.E., C.M.G., M.C., M.D., F.R.C.P.

*Formerly: Director of Medical Services, Hong Kong, 1937-47;
Governor and C.-in-C. of the Seychelles, 1947-51; Principal
Medical Officer, Ministry of Health, 1951-56.*

It was time for this book to be written, and I am very glad that
Liam Nolan has written it. Since the end of the Second World
War we have been subjected to a flood of books and films whose
main message appears to be that 'the only good Jap is a dead
Jap'. That this message is sheer nonsense must be evident to any
thinking person, but I am happy that the still, small voice of
protest should be that of 'Uncle John' Watanabe, whose courage
and humanity were an inspiration to so many of us in the darkest
days of the war.

When I was organising relief for prisoners of war and interned civilians after the fall of Hong Kong before being myself
picked up for 'treatment' by the Kempeitai, the Japanese
version of the Gestapo, I was helped by several Japanese who,
like Uncle John, had no notions of disloyalty to their own
country, but who were appalled by the conditions in the camps
and anxious to do all they could to relieve unnecessary suffering. Some were tortured; some executed. Uncle John, I am
thankful to say, escaped, but he would be the first to want this
book about him to be a tribute to that group of humanitarian
Japanese of whom he was the most outstanding.

Nolan deserves great credit for his amazing industry in securing the detailed information which enabled him to paint so vivid a picture of Uncle John's boyhood and early life before he took up his Christian ministry. The author succeeds also in giving the reader an authentic picture of Uncle John's wonderful courage when carrying out the very hazardous operation of taking badly needed medical and food supplies into the prisoner of war camp at Shamshui Po. His courage was all the more remarkable because, and I can vouch for this, he was absolutely terrified, knowing full well the punishment that would be meted out to him if he were caught.

Shortly after the fall of Hong Kong in 1941, I pleaded with the Japanese High Command to allow the Red Cross to operate in Hong Kong, but it was over a year before this was granted. In the meantime, all we were allowed to do was to set up an informal welfare committee with representatives in the main civilian internment camps, and no official links were permitted with the military camps. Funds were generously provided by Chinese, Indians, Portuguese, Eurasians and Third Nationals, and although the money was used strictly for humanitarian purposes, the donors knew full well that their generosity exposed them to punishment for pro-British sympathies. In fact the chief manager of the Hong Kong and Shanghai Bank and his senior executive who helped organise the fund died of ill-treatment in prison, another banker was executed and many donors suffered a similar fate.

But their generosity enabled food, clothes, bedding, seeds, books, drugs, surgical instruments and many other necessities to be sent to the people in the camps, many of whom had been interned with nothing but the clothes they stood in. Funds for rent, food, clothes, medical and dental services and schooling were provided for orphanages, for the two Chinese hospitals not taken over by the Japanese and for the outside families of those interned or in prison. And once I had managed to get a list of survivors of the December fighting, I was able to organise groups of Chinese and Third Nationals to carry regular parcels of food and medicine to the prisoner of war camps, addressed to different prisoners each time. But there were obvious gaps, especially when escape attempts took place and the Japanese Camp Commandant stopped parcel privileges for weeks, sometimes months at a time, leaving the prisoners in a desperate state for lack of essential protective foods. Then they developed a variety of deficiency diseases, and frequently succumbed to enteritis and diphtheria.

It was at this stage that Nellie Lee put me in touch with Uncle John, one of the camp interpreters, who agreed to take in anti-diphtheritic serum, milk powder, sulpha drugs, vitamins and funds which the camp medical officers could use to bribe prison guards to buy essential protein and vitamin foods to supplement their very deficient diet, and seeds to grow vegetables, etc. inside the camp. It cannot be too clearly stated that these funds were used purely to relieve suffering in the camps. Never was Uncle John asked, nor would he have agreed, to supply prisoners with the means to escape or in any way to further the British war effort. But there are many prisoners alive today who owe their lives to his brave Samaritan smuggling.

The author has furnished several letters in facsimile written by British officials and others on the outstanding services of Uncle John during the Japanese occupation.

It is a tragic irony of Fate that this man, of all others, should later have suffered so cruelly. He deserved, and has, our deepest sympathy for his dreadful loss.

Not long ago Uncle John appeared on a 'This Is Your Life' programme on BBC Television. I met him afterwards for the first time since the end of the war. After dining him at my home in Hampstead, I took him back to his hotel near Lancaster Gate Tube Station. On emerging from the station we were stopped three times in the street by people who had watched the television programme on the previous evening, and who asked Uncle John if they might shake him by the hand, saying they recognised him as the Japanese officer-interpreter who had helped British P.O.W.'s and civilian internees so splendidly with such disregard for his own safety during the Pacific War.

161

Most touching is an incident the author relates in a Note at the beginning of the book. It concerns a waitress who was brought to her senses by the television programme featuring Uncle John.

If this book can achieve the same result with its readers as the television programme did for the waitress, it will go some way, and the way that Uncle John would want most, to rewarding Kiyoshi Watanabe for his great service to humanity.